"...but that's another story"

by Bernard Dwyer

Dave Mallinson Publications 1995

"...but that's another story"
From Dave Mallinson Publications
First published in England 1995 by Dave Mallinson Publications
3 East View
Moorside
Cleckheaton
West Yorkshire
England
BD19 6LD
Telephone 01274 876388
Facsimile 01274 852280

Copyright © Bernard Dwyer 1995

ISBN 1 899512 15 2 (paperback)
ISBN 1 899512 17 9 (hardback)

**British Library Cataloguing in Publication Data. A catalogue
record for this book is available from the British Library**

Typesetting and layout by David J Taylor
Word processing and proof reading by Julie Taylor
Jacket design by David J Taylor and Bryan Ledgard
Illustrations by Flemming Christofferson, used with permission
Paperback jacket photograph of Bernard Dwyer by Peter Fawcett
Text set in 10 point Adobe Caslon
Printed and bound by Watkiss Studios, Biggleswade, Bedfordshire

ACKNOWLEDGEMENTS

Bernard Dwyer wishes to thank most sincerely the following for their very kind help and co-operation in the production of this book:

John Ferguson, for his continued efforts in persuading me to have some of my literary work published

Maureen Ferguson, for her careful scrutiny of my work

Christine Byrne, for her unstinting efforts, help and publicity

Mary C Dwyer, for the introduction

Flemming Christofferson, for kind permission to use his illustrations

Julie Taylor, for her expert proofing and typing

David J Taylor, for his strenuous efforts to have the book typeset and published on schedule

also

The Leeds branch of Comhaltas committee and its members, for their moral support

The Comhaltas headquarters, Dublin, for their best wishes and their support

"...but that's another story"

by Bernard Dwyer

Introduction

THE AUTHOR OF this collection of poems and stories, Bernard Dwyer, is no stranger in the literary field, though this is his first publication in book form. It happily coincides with the Leeds branch of Comhaltas Ceoltóirí Éireann's twenty-fifth year celebrations. Bernard has been an active member of that branch for the past twenty-five years. In the early 1980s he was responsible for the successes of some of Leeds' early *scoraíochts*.

Bernard Dwyer's name has been prominent in the controversial letter columns of "The Irish Post", "The Roscommon Herald", "The Western People" and "The Roscommon Champion". His entries into short story writing competitions, some of which appear in this book, have received many commendations over the years. The author also has had several articles published in the Comhaltas magazine "An Treoir" which is read internationally.

It is his talent for combining fiction interwoven with fact which makes his stories so true to life. He also has a gift of bringing his native countryside alive by painting detailed cameos of nature which remain indelibly printed on the mind. A great love of history and folklore is also present - learned as a young boy at his grandmother's knee.

By the glowing turf fire in the kitchen, tales were told and legends learned which in later years would run like ribbons throughout his writings, the many coloured strands of fiction, fact and fairytales all being brought together and tied into one inescapable truth - a great love of all things Irish.

Story-telling is becoming a very much revived artform in Ireland and this book helps to reinforce this movement. Obviously the stories within this book will not escape the eyes of the critics - no views worth writing about ever do. In my eye, this is a book that should be read wherever Irish people or people who love Ireland are to be found. They will be the richer for the experience.

Mary C Dwyer
December 1994

Contents

PREFACE
by
Bernard Dwyer

"Born in the midst of
rare scenery and fairy forts"

I was born June 1916 in a townland near friendly Frenchpark in the County Roscommon, Ireland. I am the second oldest of a family of fourteen, some of whom have passed on to their eternal reward. My earliest recollections are of the long summer childhood days that I spent roaming the flowery meadows and sweet scenting heather of our thirty acre farm. Those were the days when songbirds were more plentiful than they are today. Artificial dressings on the soil killed off many of those extremely entertaining songsters.

The southern view from our house was curtained by a steep hill. But the very unique enchanting views to the north, the east and the west more than compensated for this disadvantage. There were the deep blue Ox mountains and scenic County Mayo, rising majestically away to the west. Directly north, one could view the silvery hills of beloved County Sligo, particularly as they glittered in a mid-day summer's sun. In their centre was a dome-shaped hill called "Keash". Towering impressively above its sister hills, it forever stands guard over the precious spot where sleeps the immortal remains of William Butler Yeats.

In the course of my youthful and carefree years, those same inspiring surroundings had a strange fascinating effect upon my vision and upon the Great Being who created it. To me, it was then and still is, the designing work of the Master's Hand. To gaze in the direction of the Ox mountains, particularly when the red setting sun was poised on its tip and casting multi-coloured shadows across an enchanting countryside was, to say the least, heavenly.

Another strange coincidence from which I got much pleasure and inspiration was that there were two *fairy forts* adjacent to our house. The very same *forts* had a deep-down inspiring effect upon my maternal grandmother, who lived with us and who was born in that very same house one hundred and fifty years ago. Many of the fairy-tales that I have written are based on her great art and style of story-telling. Regretfully, that is an art which seemed at one time to be dying. But thank God, it is now being revived.

So impressed was I by the makebelieve style of my grandmother's fairy-tales that in my childhood days I made frequent visits to the nearby fairy forts, invariably before sunset. According to my grandmother, sunset was the time when the fairies were out and about. On countless occasions in my childish imagination, I really did see fairies scurrying amidst the flowery undergrowth of the same forts. I would then return to our house as fast as my bare feet could carry me and inform my grandmother and the other members of our family, of my latest encounter with the fairies. Of course during the winter months, when the hawthorn would have lost its bloom and the bare branches would have become eyesores, the little people would have gone into hibernation and it would then be the time for fireside stories.

Myself and my younger brothers and sisters would sit around the large, sparkling and colourful turf fire and listen breathlessly to our grandmother's stories. Not all of her stories were about fairies. In keeping with most of the people of her generation, my grandmother was a great historian. She could delve away beyond the misty space of seventeen hundred years, to the time that Saint Patrick brought Christianity and Faith to Ireland. She could also relate stories of the sages and bards of ancient Ireland. My grandmother also had a great knowledge of the Brehan laws, laws that are studied by many scholars even in this day and age.

Fairy lore was instilled in my blood at a very young age. The art of story-telling I had acquired in my early teens. The collection of stories contained in this book are a mixture of fact and fiction. I sincerely hope that you will find that the factual stories are just as interesting as the creative ones. I attribute my ability to record and create such stories to a family tradition and a God-given good memory.

Bernard Dwyer
December 1994

A Grandmother's influence

THE VAST MAJORITY of English people I've made contact with over the past three decades are, invariably, proud to boast of the Irish grandmother. Strangely enough only a tiny minority refer to their Irish grandfather. I think that the main reason for this marked discrepancy is not that the gap between their grandmothers and their grandfathers is that wide, but that their grandmother's influence is by far the greatest.

Perhaps I'm basing this theory on the fact that I was greatly influenced by my paternal grandmother, an influence that has stayed with me all of my long life although she has passed on to her eternal reward almost fifty-five years ago. In the course of family gatherings, or over a pint with my many friends, I have quoted my grandmother's logic and vision on countless occasions. She was just typical of most grandmothers.

It was at my grandmother's knee, sitting on a low stool that I learned how to write in a childish way long before I commenced school. It was she who taught me my first lessons in Ireland's "noble history", as she called it. She always placed very strict emphasis on learning how to "think deeply". 'Writing and reading will come natural', she'd say.

Though educated at what she described as "a glorified hedge school" she had acquired a wonderful art of story-telling. And many's the cold winter's night we sat in front of a glowing turf fire and listened breathlessly to her tales of Irish battles that were fought and won - and lost.

There were heart rending stories of the famine years as well as moving stories of children taken away with the fairies. There was also the story of "Ould" Betty McGinty, who lived up on the mountain. She'd got the power to get a child returned by the fairies.

There were the grand stories of kind stepmothers who lived to be a very ripe old age and of course the "wicked ones" who'd have muck thrown in their faces by the children's dead mother, should they dare to go out after dark. There were plenty of tales of men who gave "back answers" to the priest. Either their mares died foalin' or else their cows were found upside down in a deep boghole.

However, so much for those children's stories, there was also a great sincere side to my grandmother. She loved our Irish culture and herself was a grand sean-nós singer. She'd remember céilís being broken up by the law. Then there was the "lilters' gatherings", where young and old gathered for a session of what was called "puss music". Those were, according to my grandmother, the best sessions of the lot.

My grandmother was steeped in Irish history. She hadn't much time for politics. "A crooked game" she called it. She loved to talk at length of the period of Ireland's "Golden Age", from the time of Saint Patrick to the coming of the Vikings: a period of three hundred years when the Irish monks and scholars covered themselves with glory on the continent. The period in which they earned for Ireland the title of "The Land of Saints and Scholars".

It was the period when wealthy people sent their children from England and the continent to be educated in Ireland. The period of unrest that followed she would describe as "The dogs that bite the hands that fed them". She was born in the famine years. And though they lived on a small patch of ground in a white-washed cabin, they got enough to eat to enable them to survive and grow up to be strong.

"Anyone with a real sincere trust in God survived to tell the tale."

May her kind soul rest in peace.

The day a bodhrán
shocked an army

My EARLIEST RECOLLECTIONS are of a Christmas morning. It was the
year 1920. I awoke earlier than usual, sneaked out of bed and made my way
to the kitchen in almost total darkness. I was just four-and-a-half years old.
A silvery light from the wintry moon, shining through the kitchen window,
illuminated the open fireplace. My stocking hung on the black crook where I
had confidently placed it the night before. On closer examination I discovered that a large Christmas stocking was attached to mine by means of a
safety-pin.

'Santa!' I shouted in a tone of voice that was a little too sharp at that unearthly hour.

My grandmother joined me almost immediately.

'Keep that voice of yours down', she whispered, 'or you'll wake the young ones.' She got the big Christmas candle alight and then commenced to get the turf fire started while I set about finding out what Santa had stuffed into the large silver-coloured stocking.

There were a number of interesting items, including a tiny pack of cards which was, so far, the least of my surprises.

As I delved a bit deeper I came up with a fairly large wooden box which, to my delight, contained a number of tiny soldiers, each holding his gun at the ready.

'Santa must have read my thoughts', I murmured. 'This was the present I really wanted.'

My grandmother, being a noted story-teller, had instilled into my tiny mind many hair-raising tales of battles that were fought and won in different parts of Ireland. The impact of her heroic stories had aroused in me a deep longing to have my own private army. In the weeks and months that followed, the number of successful battles that I had to my credit would put Red Hugh O'Donnel to shame.

It was about six months after that memorable Christmas morning, on a roasting day in late June, I was strolling carefree through one of our meadow fields. My chief interests were the countless butterflies as they winged their way noiselessly from one flower to another. They were followed in turn by the busy bees as they went about their scientific rounds of extracting honey from the numerous wild flowers. The skylarks also attracted my attention as they soared higher and higher into the clear blue sky; lilting their jigs, reels and hornpipes before descending to the spot from which they started off.

My nature study was interrupted by my dad as he appeared in another part of the field complete with scythe and sharpening stone. He seemed oblivious of my presence and commenced to "whet" the scythe. I always admired the expert manner in which my dad slid the stone along each side of the blade in turn. The musical sounds that this skill produced had the effect of cancelling the magical music which came from the skylarks. However, it did have the effect of arousing the skylarks into action.

I moved in the direction of my dad who by this time had finished sharpening his scythe and had started to cut the grass. I had only moved a few paces when the unusually strong voice of a man shouting,

'Make it snappy!' drew my curious attention. I looked in the direction from which the shouting came and to my amused surprise I saw a long line of real soldiers approaching. They all had guns at the ready just like the ones Santa brought to me at Christmas.

I then noticed that a large body of men who were dressed like my dad were marching in front of the soldiers. I looked in the direction of where my dad was and noticed that he was leaning comfortably on his scythe, admiring the approaching army. As they drew near, one of the soldiers pointed at my dad and shouted,

'Fall in!'

By this time I had reached my dad. We both joined the men who were in front of the soldiers and marched towards our house.

'Halt!' was called.

We were all herded into our front garden. A number of soldiers were put guarding us. The remainder removed their gear and sat in the field outside of the garden drinking from large bottles. I was later separated from the men in the garden and allowed to mix with the soldiers, a number of whom entered our house and commenced to search for guns that were not there.

In the course of their ransacking, they became very suspicious of something that tossed about within my mother's melodeon. They were about to pull it apart when my grandmother intervened to say that in the course of repairs a worn-out spare part had been left inside. The officer accepted her explanation and the old melodeon lived to play many jigs, reels and horn-pipes in the months and years that followed.

One of the men in the garden called through the open kitchen window and asked for a drink of buttermilk. My mother and grandmother commenced to hand out mugs of fresh buttermilk through the open window. The soldiers too joined in the feast and before they left the churn was empty.

However, a few minutes later something sensational was to happen that became a talking topic in the district in the years that followed. One of the soldiers accidentally knocked the old bodhrán from its wooden peg above the fireplace. It created such a thundering noise as it hopped along the flagged floor that the soldiers who were out in the field jumped to attention - guns at the ready - while the others who were guarding the men in the garden discharged a number of shots above their heads!

Later, I leaned against the old iron gate and watched the army and my dad, together with the other men, fade from view. I also thought of 'my army' tucked behind one of the plates on the dresser. It was the end of, up until then, my brilliant military career. That night I lay awake for hours try-ing to figure out the whereabouts of my dad.

I awoke the next morning - to the familiar sounds of his voice in the kitchen! After breakfast we both went again to the same meadow field we'd been taken from the day before. My dad commenced to 'whet' the scythe. I resumed my nature study. It all seems such a long time ago... I sometimes think of it as a dream. The old house has disappeared long ago, but the but-terflies and bees still float from flower to flower, as the musical skylarks chant their crisp notes in salute, above that hallowed spot.

Around the road to school

As I SCRAMBLED out of bed on a memorable day seventy-two years ago, there was a huge lump in my throat. It is one morning that I'll always remember. I made my weary way towards our large kitchen, where my mother was busy preparing breakfast. My grandmother took me gingerly by the hand and led me in the direction of a small wooden tub which was filled with steaming warm water. She then commenced to wash my face and hands with a soft soapy cloth, taking particular care with my ears.

'A clean face and dirty ears is like a clean collar above a dirty shirt', she said. Of course I was always very reluctant at having my ears washed.

By the time my grandmother had finished with me, my mother invited me to come and have my breakfast which consisted of homemade bread, homemade butter and a large blue duck egg. This was one morning that I could have very well done without the duck egg. I had spent the previous couple of years roaming the familiar fields with my father, or perhaps tumbling in the brown, sweet-smelling heather of our thirty acre farm. Besides, it was the glorious month of June and I had just celebrated my sixth birthday.

After I'd finished my breakfast my mother placed a new satchel (which my grandmother had bought from a travelling salesman a few weeks earlier) upon my shoulder then kissed me tenderly and made a quick retreat towards the "small room". My grandmother stood staring at me with tear-filled eyes, although not quite as tear-filled as mine were. It was at this stage that my father entered by the back door carrying a white pail filled with frothy milk which he had just taken from the "kicking" cow. The same cow had to be "strapped" before milking or else she would kick the stars out of the sky.

My father then placed his big heavy hand upon my shoulder and said in that familiar soft voice of his,

'Son!...after you get out from school hurry home...you know we have that field of hay to gather.' He then made a smart exit through the door he'd come in. My mother then emerged from the "small room", took me by the hand and we both set out walking down the narrow, mossy boreen, which was ornamented on both sides with hedges of sweet-smelling hawthorn. This boreen led to the road which was to take me to that old glorified "hedge-school" as my grandmother used to call it.

On reaching the road I tearfully parted with my mother. For the first time in my six years I was on my own. I gazed for a few moments at the nearby "fairy fort" on my left. I wondered if the "little people" knew that I was heading off in the direction of that other fairy fort which I had to pass before reaching the Callaghan farmhouse. There, the oldest girl of the Callaghan family, Nora, was waiting to take me in hand.

Before I'd reached the other fairy fort, I stopped to admire a herd of red deer which stood on a height within the distant deer park that belonged to the local baron Lord de Freyne. This enchanting view took my mind off the school, at least momentarily. I walked smartly in the direction of the fort with its circles of blooming hawthorn. Several brown rabbits stood upon their hind legs to gaze on a budding scholar who was oblivious of what lay in store. About fifty yards on was the Callaghan farmhouse.

As I arrived at the small gate which led into a neatly kept flower-garden, Tom Callaghan, who was hoeing a cabbage plot close to the flower-garden, came to the little gate and ushered me into his kitchen. There was Jack who was older than me, Nora who was appointed to be my "bodyguard" and Anny who was about my age, all ready and awaiting my arrival before setting off for school. I would like to add that this man Tom

Callaghan was a very good friend of my father and I had often been to Callaghan's before, especially during the hay-carrying season when my father and Tom Callaghan worked in company.

We all set out walking in the direction of the school. Nora held my hand tightly all of the way.

It was the beginning of a friendship which has, thank God, lasted to this very day. Nora was a maternal, kind person who had lost her mother at a very young age and, being the oldest girl, assumed the responsibility of caring for the other members of the family. There were two more sisters at this particular time who had not commenced school. Even to this very day, whenever I visit Ireland, a call to Nora is a must. There, a warm welcome is always awaiting me. It is a friendship that has lasted over seventy years.

As we rounded a bend called Alec Street, the old school building came into view. It was a long low building with six large ten-paned windows. This was a two-roomed school with two teachers - one male, the other female. The headmaster, Terence Rodgers, was a tall man with fair hair and a very red nose. He was, I was later to learn, a very good teacher but I never really got to like the canes he had put away in the little desk in the corner of the room. The windows of this school were so high up that it was impossible to see outside. You could hear voices and after a while get to know to whom the particular voices belonged. I suppose you could call the place a prison.

The lady teacher to whom I was assigned was called Miss Murren. She was a neatly dressed girl who always wore a small, black-faced watch hung around her neck by means of a silver chain. She always held a cane in her left hand, but seldom if ever used it. If she did decide to punish you, it was by means of a hard knuckle; and by hell, she did have a very hard knuckle. She was a brilliant teacher.

There were two maps in one schoolroom and three in the other. One was a map of Ireland, the other a map of the world. The largest map in the school was that of Britain. It was much larger than the other maps and for a number of years this gave me the belief that Britain was much larger than the rest of the world. A picture of an Irish elk hung between the map of the world and the map of Britain. It seemed to my tender mind to be the only civilised thing in the room.

A large printed notice was placed upon what was called "the back wall". I was later to learn that it was to the effect that compulsory Irish was introduced by the first Irish government after the Treaty of 1922. The problem was that none of the teachers knew a word of Irish. This really solved a problem for me, at least for the space of three months. The school was

9

closed down for those three months while the teachers were doing a course in Irish.

The Irish language had been outlawed for countless years and would have died a natural death were it not for the heroic efforts of a very great Irishman and scholar Douglas Hyde, who had a price on his head for years by an outside power. Douglas Hyde lived to become the first President of Ireland in later years. I must add here that although we do have a native government for over seventy years, little has been done to bring about a revival of our native tongue.

I did spend a very happy three months with my father in the green fields of our small farm until, lo and behold, the teachers came back from their "school" by the end of September. We were given a long lecture by the head teacher about how we were supposed to "take great pains" with our Irish from then on. We were later to learn what the pains really meant. The pains invariably came from one of the canes he had carefully put away in the little press.

The trouble was that it eventually transpired that the "sputtering" of Irish that our teachers acquired in their short course was not real Irish, with the result that by the time I'd finished school, I discovered that my Irish lessons were a waste of time - as were our teachers' - and being compelled to learn our dying language was a disaster. It should be made an optional subject with trophies or medals awarded at the end of the year for the best workers.

Today, we have a great cultural organisation, Comhaltas Ceoltóirí Éireann, which has done a marvellous job of reviving our great national talents: talents which too were outlawed, at one period. Children of very tender ages flock to learn their native music, song and dance and with the advent of Cúlra, their history as well.

Some treasured stones

IN MY CHILDHOOD days I developed a craze for stone collecting. That doesn't mean that I tried to pick up every stone I came across. My kind of stone had to be rather tiny, of certain dimensions, such as round or almost round, or preferably oval-shaped. Being born close to Lough Gara, which separates Roscommon from Sligo at one point, it was along the rocky shores of this lough I invariably found the type of stone that I was looking for.

It was only after I'd read of the famous Blarney Stone that my interest in fancy stone-collecting came to an abrupt ending. As most people throughout the civilised world are aware, anybody who has had the privilege and courage to kiss The Blarney ended up with an unique gift of wit and speech. The millions who have done so have discovered for themselves that there is, however, a slight difference between "kissing the Blarney" and kissing a girl or boy beneath the mistletoe, on a Hallowe'en night when ghosts are most active.

Of course, there is another stone which has been very dear to the hearts of Irish people the world over, particularly to the hearts of traditional music lovers. They would be extremely angry if I neglected to mention it. In my youth, I would have given my bottom dollar to sit upon the same stone and try to "note-out" a few jigs and reels. The trouble was, I never could get as far as the bottom dollar! You've already guessed: it is, of course, the one "Outside Dan Murphy's Door".

But the stone that I really wish to write about is, indeed, very far removed from the ones I've just mentioned. It's rather funny that when a man starts "knocking on" he will remember all or most of the things of his childhood, whilst at the same time he might spend ages looking for his oul' pipe behind the plates on the dresser and it carefully placed in the corner of his mouth.

And now to get down to the stone I had in mind till I commenced to dream of my childhood. The history of this particular stone dates back thousands of years. In actual fact, it goes much further back than the period in which Ireland was Christianised. However, I've got to start somewhere, so I could scarcely find a period more appropriate than 254 a.d. when Cormac Mac Art was crowned Ard Rí (High King) of All-Ireland. He was crowned upon the very stone about which I'm going to tell you.

It will be of deep interest to you to learn that the equivalent of our Fleadh Cheoil na hÉireann, our annual festival of traditional music, was held on the same day as the Ard Rí's Coronation. Scholarships were awarded to all musical winners. Special honours were also conferred upon the most distinguished of the Bards (poets) and also the Brehans (law-givers) whose laws were the most just in Europe at that period.

Now, as every school-child knows, Scotland's first kings were of course Irish. This is where the stone that I had in mind at the start comes in. It was as a gesture of goodwill that the Ard Rí of All-Ireland, had Ireland's Coronation Stone sent to Scotland for the big occasion. The coronation ceremony in question took place at a place in Scotland called Scone. The Irish Coronation Stone lingered there for some time and became known as the "Stone of Scone".

The English were in one respect much like myself. They too were fond of collecting stones - amongst other things of course. It happened at a period of "understanding" or "misunderstanding" in English/Scottish relationships that the English got hold of the Irish Coronation Stone and took it back to London. Several English Kings and Queens, including the present Queen Elizabeth, have been crowned upon it. This should serve as a warning to all musicians to be very careful about who you lend your valuable musical instruments to. Or it's like lending a valuable book - you seldom get it back.

The proper name for the Irish Coronation Stone is Lia Fail, meaning Stone of Destiny. Some people tell me that Lia Fail is Hebrew. What do you think? Here's a hint: try spelling it backwards.

Big Tom Keane and the fairies

LONG, LONG AGO in the good old days when men chewed tobacco and swallows built their nests in old mens' beards, there lived a huge giant of a man called Big Tom Keane. Tom lived in a very remote area and close to a large "fairy fort". Tom and his wife Kitty had but one child - a son whom they called Tomás Og. Naturally they cherished little Tomás Og very dearly, especially in view of the fact that Kitty had a very hard time during the birth of Tomás Og and furthermore the local doctor had told both Tom and Kitty that they could have no more of a family.

Tomás Og developed into a beautiful child. Indeed he was so handsome that the local midwife - or handywoman as she was called in those far off days - warned Tom and Kitty to keep little Tomás Og away from the fairy fort, especially towards sunset. They did this until he'd reached the age of five years; and most people know, five years is an age when it is almost impossible to keep after a child all of the time.

Now to make a long story short, Big Tom was a great fiddle player and every evening towards sunset, he would take down the fiddle and thrash out jigs, reels and hornpipes galore. The most reason why he did this was to keep Tomás Og's attention away from the "little people". The music did the trick for a couple of years until one evening as the red sun was sinking below the distant mountain, didn't a cousin of Big Tom's call and with the excitement his visit caused, Big Tom and Kitty forgot all about Tomás Og and the little people who lived and played soft music at the back of Keane's house, occasionally at midnight. This cousin of Big Tom's was also a man who loved his music and although he could not play any musical instrument himself, he was a very good lilter.

They were in deep conversation about the good old days - and also the bad ones - when all of a sudden Big Tom's cousin said,

'Yarrah, to the devil with the good and bad times, give us a tune on the old fiddle, Big Tom, and I'll join you with my "puss music". '

'Very well then,' said Big Tom and he jumped up and grabbed the old fiddle from its resting place above the mantle.

Tom commenced to tune the old fiddle while Kitty hung the large kettle upon a crook of the huge crane which stood above a sparkling turf fire. The "lilter Quinn" as he was affectionately called, took his place beside Big Tom and started to do his bit of tuning, for believe it or not, a lilter does have to tune even that there is no musical instrument involved. In a matter of seconds they were at it "hammer and tongs" while Kitty, who was a very good dancer as well as a singer, kept time with the music as she prepared the tay for the two men.

Kitty was about to pass on two mugs of tay to the men - they'd just finished the tune called "The Goat in the Bog" - when who should come rushing into the kitchen but old Maggie Sally and her panting like a race horse that would be after winning the Grand National. Her forlorn looking appearance standing there in the middle of the flag-floor soon brought the fiddling and lilting to a sudden end.

'Have you seen what's happening in the fairy fort?' asked Maggie with a deep sigh.

'What the devil *is* happening in the fairy fort?' shouted Big Tom and although Big Tom was a gruff type of a man, he was known as having a "heart of gold".

'There are lights the colour of a rainbow spinning all around and a strong wind blowing within the fort although it is deadly calm elsewhere.'

'Where's Tomás Og?' screamed Kitty at the top of her voice.

Big Tom put the fiddle down on the kitchen table and made a dash for the door. The lilter Quinn had nothing to put away, so he jumped up and followed Big Tom. Kitty was quick on their heels and poor Maggie Sally, being a bit feeble, sauntered out after them. Kitty could be heard screaming away in the distance...

'Tomás Og, Tomás Og...' Naturally, the screams of Kitty brought the neighbours from near and eventually from afar.

It was now long after sunset and until dawn next morning Big Tom, Kitty, Lilter Quinn and all the neighbours of Pullbawn - for that was the name of the townland where the Keane family lived - searched high and low, but neither sight nor light of little Tomás Og was to be seen. In fact again to make a long story short, poor little Tomás Og Keane was never seen again, at least by his broken-hearted mother. However, Big Tom did get a glimpse of him later.

In the years that followed Big Tom would set out for the fairy fort, his fiddle tucked under his oxter, as the sun would be gently setting beyond the distant hill. He would sit upon an old decayed tree stump and play lonely laments, occasionally stopping to call out to the fairies to bring back his long lost son Tomás Og. This Big Tom did night after night, despite the fact that his wife Kitty made every effort to stop him, on the advice of the local parish priest.

Youngsters returning from a dance often stopped to hear Big Tom's lonely laments and his heart-rending calls to the fairies of Pullbawn to please bring back his son. The vast majority of the local people did not believe that the fairies had little Tomás Og. However, there were some of the older people who had other ideas. People who believed that in the distant past such beings as fairies did in fact exist. Strangely enough they were proven to be right as time went on.

One night as the local priest was returning from attending a sick man, he was flabbergasted on seeing multi-coloured lights spinning all around the fairy fort.

The incident put a turning point in the Big Tom Keane controversy. While the good priest did not make "a song and dance" about what he had seen on that particular night in the fairy fort of Pullbawn, he was very sympathetic towards Big Tom and Kitty ever afterwards.

Then one night, a long time after the priest's vision of the fairy light, as a group of elderly men were returning home after a game of cards, they were spellbound by what they saw on approaching the fairy fort. It suddenly became illuminated with multi-coloured light. Moments later they heard the lonely lament of a fiddle upon which was played a most beautiful tune. It was only when the beautiful voice of Kitty, Big Tom's wife reached their ears, that they realised that the fiddler was indeed none other than Big Tom himself. The song that Kitty was singing was of course "The Fairy Child"...

"A mother came while stars were paling, wailing round a lonely spring;
Thus she cried as tears were falling, calling on the Fairy King.
Why with spells my child caressing, courting him with fairy joy;
Why destroy a mother's blessing, wherefore steal my baby boy."

The music and singing came to an abrupt halt. Then the voice of Big Tom could be heard shouting:

'Oh, there he is Kitty! There he is! I have seen him Kitty.' Then the voice of Kitty was heard saying:

'Will you for God's sake come home Tom Keane?'

'I'm tellin' you Kitty, for a split second I saw our little Tomás Og...'

'Please come home with me Tom' pleaded Kitty.

They both walked away from the fairy fort singing the last verse of "The Fairy Child"...

"In vain my plaintive calling, tears are falling down like rain;
He now sports with fairy pleasure, he's the treasure of their train.
Fare thee well my child forever, in this world I've lost my joy;
But in Heaven we ne'er shall sever, there I'll find my angel boy."

So ends the sad story of Big Tom Keane and his wife Kitty.

The legend of the fort that disappeared

LONG, LONG AGO, before my great grandmother's time, there stood a huge fort in an isolated part of north Roscommon. This unique fort was surrounded by a mixture of hawthorn and holly hedge. It was a meeting place for Fenians who would assemble at midnight when the moon would be full, to report on "moon's progress".

It must be remembered that in those days people always prayed to the new moon and hoped that its four weeks duration would bring about a change in their oppressed situation. Indeed, it was the good Saint Patrick himself that was responsible for this pagan custom.

As most people know, before the gifted saint arrived in Ireland, it was a pagan country where people adored many things including the moon. However, before his death, the old people would tell you, Saint Patrick permitted a certain amount of pagan customs to remain, believing that to strip people of their traditions would deprive them of their souls.

Now it was upon the forts of Ireland that stood noble wooden buildings which were the homes of kings and lesser noblemen and women in the days of Saint Patrick. With the passage of time those buildings, together with their owners, disappeared. Today nothing remains but some foundation stones of sites where the harp and the lute and indeed many other musical instruments echoed o'er the valleys.

This unusual Roscommon fort was one such site before my great grandmother's time. In those far off days it was a meeting place for courting couples - yes they did court in those days too - but it was a strange kind of courting where the girl would spend most of the long evening playing with her lover's watch-chain, which hung like a clothesline across a large double breasted waistcoat!

It was also a meeting place for céilí sessions, when the youth of the nearby townlands would assemble on the night of the new moon to pass the night until dawn next morning, competing in music, song and dance. There were also the story-telling competitions which were very much a part of Irish functions, even in my father and mother's time.

Lo and behold, it was after the old widow, upon whose land this fort stood, was evicted from her humble cabin by the local landlord, that the troubles commenced. To add insult to injury, this same lord-of-the-manor issued an order prohibiting assemblies of any kind in or around the fort in question.

It was on the night of the first new moon after this callous eviction and prohibition order that strange things began to happen. As the locals were leaving the rambling house after a game of "twenty-five", they were alarmed by the sound of clogs coming from the narrow boreen which led from the Fort of Sheemore, which the fort was called by the locals.

Little did the gamblers think that the two men were none other than the landlord's henchmen who were sent by the old tyrant himself to guard the fort against any would-be intruders. Panting with fear and exhaustion, the two began to relate their hair-raising experiences within the forbidden grounds of Sheemore!

Their first experience was the gentle playing of a harp which got louder and louder, until it was joined by the wailing of a banshee close by. Then from the midst of the thicket emerged countless fairies. The banshee ceased to wail, instead the music of many musical instruments filled the fort as well as the countryside.

On hearing of this strange goings-on, the old tyrant suspected that it was a trick by what he termed "the cunning of the Irish peasants". So, he issued an order that every stone, bush, root and branch be removed from the fort and dumped into Lough Gara.

Next morning as dozens of the old tyrant's workmen, horses and carts arrived at the fort, it had disappeared!

It was about the same time that a fort appeared upon the lands of a very humane landlord in County Meath...

'round peaceful Carrowreagh

Carrowreagh is my native place, where my family were born.

One pleasant morning early in the merry month of May;
Song birds they sang so cheerily and lambkins they did play.
My native land I left behind and slowly moved away;
From lush pasture fields and woodlands grand 'round peaceful
                                                    Carrowreagh.
It was next morning early, I reached Brittania's shore,
Bereft of friends and kith and kin, some I may see no more.
In strange surroundings, here I am, my thoughts do oft times stray;
To lush pasture fields and woodlands grand 'round peaceful
                                                    Carrowreagh.
Good fortune's light did beam on me, if only for a while;
Then death it took my bosom friend - I daily miss her smile.
Now if ever I return again, 'tis alone I'll have to stray;
In lush pasture fields and woodlands grand 'round peaceful
                                                    Carrowreagh.
Old Yorkshire's pleasant charming dales, are lovely for to view;
By poet and writer, they're admired - and envied by the few.
Still my soul steals back, to hallowed ground where sheep and cattle
                                                            stray;
In lush pasture fields and woodlands grand 'round peaceful
                                                    Carrowreagh.
Should you decide, a trip to take, across the Irish sea;
Make sure you visit the beauty spots around old Castlerea;
Roscommon's old ruined abbeys, where monks did work and pray;
The lush pasture fields and woodlands grand 'round peaceful
                                                    Carrowreagh.

A short history of Frenchpark

There were pheasants resorting and fond lovers courting,
The hare and deer they roamed the park,
Nightingales they flew in for to sing and to harbour,
In the beautiful groves and plains of Frenchpark.

THE ABOVE LINES were written by one of Frenchpark's poets, perhaps
long over one hundred years ago. Those were the days when the Lord de
Freyne Estate was at its peak. I can indeed recall much of its beauty myself,
although it was just about to disintegrate in my early and carefree days.

Let's have a peep into the pages of history and try to unravel a combi-
nation of events which led up to the formation of this estate. It would be
presumptuous of me to even try and link this ancient and historic spot with
the people who settled along the shores of Lough Gara perhaps more than
3,500 b.c., although I will try hopefully to link the Frenchpark area with the
Clan who centuries later challenged the first settlers and succeeded in
defeating them after a prolonged and bitter struggle.

As every Irish school-child knows, the first inhabitants - as far as can
be traced - were called "The Gregraide". Their chief base was situated in Sligo in the precincts of Lough Gara. They did, however, have
fortresses throughout the wide area of what was then known as Sliabh
Lugha. Archaeologists have discovered the remains of one in Castlemore
Ballaghaderreen, formerly known as "Aileach Mor".

The tribe who waged war against The Gregraide were called "The
Ciarraidhe", who later changed their name to Ceirin. They were banished
from Ulster and according to Una Staunton's account of Sliabh Lugha,
arrived there with about 300 men. They captured places now called
Coolavin, Killaraght and Artagh (Tibohine), which later became the Barony
of Frenchpark.

It was in 964 a.d. that the Clan O'Gara challenged the Ciarraidhe and
drove them from most of their bases, which included Aileach Mor, or
Castlemore, Killaraght and Artagh. Dungar (Fort of O'Gara) must have
been adjacent to the modern Frenchpark, therefore it's reasonable to assume
that the Ciarraidhe did indeed have a fortress in that particular spot.

The Clan O'Gara held sway up until just past the mid-seventeenth century when the Cromwellian settlement brought about drastic changes. A man by the name of Patrick French acquired Dungar, together with 1,500 acres of fertile lands.

A short distance from Dungar stood the very ancient Abbey of Cloonshanvale. Within its crumbling walls there is a tombstone which has the following inscription "Pray for the soul of Patrick French who lived in this world 86 years, died at his home Dungar and buried here 14th April 1667" (see "The Heart of Ireland" by Rev P A Sharkey).

Patrick was succeeded by John French who was called An Tinearna Mor. It was he who later built the stately mansion that was to dominate the Artagh countryside for almost 300 years. It was built of brick imported from Holland to the port of Sligo and conveyed to the Dungar site by horse-drawn carts. John French had his house named "French Park House".

The French family were of Norman origin and direct descendants of Sir Hubert de Freyne who landed in Leinster with Strongbow in 1168 - hence the title Lord de Freyne. They were not aristocrats and acquired their wealth by trading. Some were Mayors of Galway City which was, I believe, their ancestral home (see Una Staunton).

John French discovered too late that he had erected his mansion far too close to the Ballina-Dublin road for aristocratic privacy. He planned a diversion by having a new stretch of road built further south. It connected up with the old road about a mile west of French Park House. It passed through the townlands of Mullen, crossing the Castlerea-Boyle road into Corskeach and joining the old road again at a point east of French Park House. (Lower Street, Frenchpark is part of the old road).

We're now left with a sizeable triangle of ground, flanked on all sides by a road. It was later noticed that a road system had been unconsciously created that never can be improved upon. Along the precincts of this triangle arose working class thatched cottages, business places and a little church. Needless to say where the town took its name from.

Today we have an expanding town made up of some brilliant houses. Its people are friendly and its business people are crafty, relaxed and very generous. It's been often said:

"People come to Frenchpark, take a liking to it, go away, but return to stay".

I was born near the ancient spot myself. It has lost some of its charm I think - but it has still got the best pint of Guinness in the land!

Callow - or Carrickbeg

CALLOW - OR CARRICKBEG as it was once called, is a townland about two miles west of Dungar or Frenchpark. It was a settlement and fortress of the MacDermotts Gall, Lords of Arteach who got their name from a Dermot Gall or Dermot the Foreigner, so called because he sided with the English Lord Deputy Edmund Butler in a raid on the O'Kellys in 1307.

The country over which they were chieftains, while subordinate to the MacDermotts of the Rock on Lough Key, was bounded by the Breedogue River, Lough Gara, the Costello country around Ballyhaunis and the wild hilly area between them and the O'Flynns of Ballinlough.

Their strongholds were at Loughglynn, Dungar near Frenchpark and Callow on Lough Gara. Callow means a low marshy meadow along a river or lake and sometimes a landing place for boats. It is first mentioned in the Annals in 1393 in connection with the Battle of Cloonmagunane between two bands of MacDermotts.

The site of the castle can still be identified in the townland of Dower (Mike Dowd's land adjoins it). In the lake opposite is the crannog-type island which possibly gave the name to Carrickbeg. The land attached to the castle ran from the townland of Sra-Cocka and the Breedogue River along the shores of Lough Gara, as far west as Lung River bogs and inland to border the land of Dungar.

The death is recorded in 1522 of Mulrooney McCormac McRory Og MacDermott, a king's son who for his years and means excelled all of the clan Mulrooney, who were living in his time on Carrickbeg. In 1526 and again in 1527 O'Donnell invaded MacDermott territory and captured the castle of Callow among others, but he did not hold them.

At some time in the early 1580s, when the MacDermotts Gall were in economic decline and disposing of their lands, Callow became the property of an Elizabethan soldier of fortune, William Clifford. Those were very disturbed times and occasionally there were arrangements between the Irish and well disposed Englishmen for protection.

Anyway, in 1585 the Composition of Connaught, which is a record of landholders, states that William Clifford had a "demesne of four quarters for his said house or town of Callow in the Barony of Boyle", at the same time that Owen and Cormack McDermott are mentioned as "of Carrickbeg".

In a James I grant of 1617 the Callow quarters are assigned to William O'Mulloy of Croghan, who was married to William Clifford's daughter Margaret, but in a 1635 survey Henry Clifford, William's grandson had four quarters of Callow - 575 acres profitable, 463 unprofitable; one quarter of Slieveroe and one of Cloonmagunane. At a later date Siobhán Clifford, Henry's mother had four quarters of Callow. This would be known as "Dower Provision" for her, which is why the townland in which the castle ruins are, is called the Dower.

After the Cromwellian wars, the Clifford lands were confiscated and passed on to the French family of Frenchpark, or Dungar at the time.

I was born in the townland of Callow 79 years ago. So were my parents and maternal grandparents. My great grandfather, Patrick Sharkey owned the townland of Sra-Cocka where the Naughton family (cousins) now live. The late John Ward (R.I.P.) owned part of the townland in later years. It is now the property of his son. The unique history of Callow does not end there. The prolonged boycott of the Callow farm is another moving story.

Waiting for "bottleblowers"

MANY OF YOU readers will have seen a play entitled "Waiting for Godot" by that brilliant writer Samuel Beckett. The story you are about to read could very well be made into a play even more interesting, at least for Irish people. Beckett, we are told, insisted on directing his own plays, having a very clear vision of how they should come over on stage.

And so it is only a man who'd been through it all that could give a clear picture of the "Callow Farm Boycott" which happened more than nine decades ago. I was very fortunate in having met with that same man over forty years ago. As most Roscommon people already know, Callow is a prosperous townland about two miles west of the friendly town of Frenchpark.

At that particular period the 575 fertile acres of Callow lands were in the possession of an absentee landlord. This fertile tract he exploited to the full by over-stocking it with cattle, sheep and geese belonging to those who were trying to eke out a living with tiny plots on the remaining 463 acres of infertile lands which bordered the "heart" of Callow.

The Callow peoples' patience began to run out, especially when news spread that the "grazing" rent was to be increased by as much as ten per cent. A meeting of all concerned was called and at the very first meeting it was unanimously decided, to use that word which the people of Mayo had given to the English language, to "boycott" the Callow farm.

Word was then circulated to all those who had cattle grazing on the farm to have them removed from the farm on a certain date. Failing to do so, their stock would be driven off the farm to a large tract of impassable bog, which lay further west but adjacent to the disputed area. Some obeyed this sudden and curt order but there were others who refused, only to find their stock partly submerged in the adjacent bog.

The local absentee landlord's agent got in touch with his lordship as fast as he could in those days. It was then noticed that extra police were being drafted into Frenchpark. The agent set about organising a publicity campaign inviting "grazees" (as they were called) from as far afield as Loughglinn to the south and Ballinameen to the east. They were of course guaranteed police protection. The cattle and sheep population began to increase on the farm, but you've guessed it, only to end up in the infertile and adjacent bog.

It looked at one period as if the boycott was going to be a failure. The police were not very optimistic with regards to its failure, having experience of the Mayo Boycott where even the British army had so recently failed.

As the pressure on the Callow men began to mount, they set about training a group of "bottleblowers" whose task it would be to warn of the arrival of police at any given time, or place. So perfect was the coded warnings of the bottleblowers that in due course they had the over-worked police at sixes and sevens.

The Callow Farm Boycott lasted for more than three years. During that time its fertile lands produced enormous crops of meadow, which receded back in to the soil, making it even more fertile and producing heavier meadow the following year. With the coming of the end of the protracted boycott, when the lands had been acquired by the Congested District Board for distribution amongst the lawless Callows, so heavy was the "butt" beneath the meadow that it was a difficult task to mow it, even with scythes.

There was a very humorous side to the Callow Farm Boycott at all times during its long drawn out struggle. Men appeared in court for being in possession of bottomless bottles similar to the ones used by the bottleblowers. However, when asked by a defending lawyer to give a demonstration of how bottles were in fact used, the police could never knock even a sound out of them. Perhaps they didn't want to.

Those who were foolish enough to put geese grazing on the farm suffered an even worse fate than those who grazed sheep and cattle. The geese invariably ended up on the tables of the boycott people. There was a cooked leg of a goose to be had in almost every house.

At the outset I stated that I was fortunate in having met a man who had been through it all. He was a retired Royal Irish Constabulary Sergeant. He was, in my honest opinion, one of the finest Irishmen I've ever come across. One night in the course of conversation over a pint, we both got to talking about the Callow Farm Boycott. The old sergeant had this to say:

'During that long drawn out boycott, my heart was always with the Callow people. They were the sincerest people I ever came across during all my years in the police force. Actually, the Callow people saved my life on many occasions. Many cold winters' nights we'd arrive at a particular "marking" and not far away from the same "marking" we'd find a bottle. Unlike the ones that the blowers were using, it had a bottom and it was filled with the lifesaving stuff...' After a long pause he went on,

'I had a job to do and they knew it. There were different ways of doing my job and both the Callow people and I knew it.' He then related to me the following humorous story:

'One night as the snow was falling outside, three of us lay in wait in an old barn where the boycott people used to hold their meetings. As the hours passed we got both very cold and bored. All of a sudden we heard a light step approaching the barn door. The door was pushed open and in walked a woman with a half-gallon can in one hand and three large brown mugs in the other. I knew the woman to be, as I thought, on our side; she had a son in the police. She passed the mugs around and then poured hot milk from the can into the large mugs. We drank greedily until the can was empty. What we did not know was that the milk was heavily laced with "potheen". In next to no time we were all fast asleep.'

'We woke at daybreak to the mad wailing of many bottleblowers. One of my lads became angry and shouted "What the hell were we doing sat here all night in the cold?" and after I rubbed the sleep from my tired eyes I replied, "Waiting for bottleblowers".'

The céilí barn and the bottleblowers

THE CÉILÍ BARN was situated in a remote corner of west Roscommon. In the early nineteenth century it was used as a meeting place for those faithful few who laboured under severe stress in order to keep our great traditions alive. Such activities were, in those days, looked upon as a cover for something of a more "sinister nature". Needless to say, they were continually hampered by the occupying forces.

In order to counter those same forces, an organisation known as the "bottleblowers" came into existence. Their job was to conceal themselves in the hills and sound the alarm by blowing into bottomless five-noggin bottles, affording the céilí people ample time to put away their instruments and make good their escape until such time as the bottleblowers would sound the all clear.

Should they decide that not all the forces had returned after a raid, they sounded a special coded alarm.

Eventually, an order was issued:

'That anyone found in possession of a bottomless bottle, would be jailed for a prolonged period.' However, this was a law which it was found impossible to enforce. The bottleblowers did a great job during the days of the immortal Michael Davitt and the Land League by warning meetings of the approach of the law.

The barn in question was built of crude stone. It had but one small window, which could easily be covered with an old sack for security reasons. A number of corn sheaves would occupy one corner, while an old barrel used in the making of potheen would occupy another. There were a couple of flails hung above the only door. There were also some ploughing chains hanging about and it is quite possible that an old cart wheel stood against one of the walls. An old winnowing riddle should about complete the furniture.

A bunch of cultural enthusiasts await in silence and semi-darkness for the bottleblowers' warning. Their only light is that of clear moon shining through the tiny window. All of a sudden there's a wailing sound among the distant hills. The music starts off. The lights are back on and in a matter of minutes the barn is alive with music and dance.

Next, the old *seanachie* takes over and for the benefit of newcomers he relates the history of the céilí barn. After him comes the sean-nós singer followed by more music and dancing. As this part of the session is reaching its climax, there's another wailing sound from the bottleblowers. This time it is a clear warning that the raiding party is on the warpath.

The session party immediately put out the lights, collect their instruments and make a quick exit. Minutes later, the raiding party enter. Some have guns while others carry lanterns. There is the usual dialogue one would expect from a raiding party in the given circumstances. Sheaves of corn are tossed about. An old useless musical instrument specially left behind for the purpose is kicked around the place. The candles and paraffin lamp are confiscated.

Having found nothing of any importance, the raiding party leave. Shortly afterwards there's another wailing sound in the distance. It is the all clear. Gradually, the céilí party enter. Candles are produced, so also is a paraffin lamp. The sheaves of corn are restored to their rightful place. After order has been restored, they get down to the nitty-gritty of what brought them here in the first place. More music, more songs and dance. It is now

30

the story-teller's turn. He relates the sad story of Ireland and her uphill battle for human and cultural rights, pointing out that one day Ireland will have the moral and financial support of a native Government.

It is thought that the late Dr Douglas Hyde, who needless to say played a leading role in the revival of our ancient Irish language, visited this barn in his younger days. Those were the days when he scoured the country in search of old people who had hung on tenaciously to their native tongue.

It is also quite possible that there were other barns or hiding places up and down the counties where dedicated Irish men and women laboured in the shadow of the law in an effort to keep the then smouldering embers of Ireland's great culture breathing.

The strange story of a Roscommon man - Edward Maxwell

Edward Maxwell was born in the townland of Runnabehy, which is adjacent to Callow and closer to Frenchpark. He was born on Christmas Day in the year 1842, one of five of a family of two brothers and three sisters. The family had been evicted from their original home in Callow by a greedy agent who wanted their lands and house for a close relative. Their only offence was being in arrears with rent which, at the time of eviction, they were ready and able to pay. Such was the law in those days.

When the absentee landlord heard of this callous eviction he was furious. He immediately ordered a house to be built on a patch of reclaimed bog to house the Maxwell family and it so happened that this patch of ground was in the townland of Runnabehy. That was how Edward happened to be born there some time later. Edward's father died in 1844, two years after Edward's birth and it fell to his wife's lot, Betty Maxwell, to raise their young family on this tiny plot of bog.

Her only means of support, apart from this small patch of ground, was the fact that she was the local midwife or "handy-woman", a profession which helped her to tide along until a year or so later when Ireland's great famine broke out. This tragedy added enormously, not just to the Maxwells' difficulties, but to thousands of other families as well.

The question that will be forever left unanswered is "How did the Maxwell family survive and grow up to be strong men and women as I will later prove?" There was no child allowance or dole in those days and it was only in the late stage of the famine, after a million people or more had died of starvation and many more had found a watery grave in coffin ships, did the English introduce the Indian meal.

Yet Edward Maxwell grew up man enough to emigrate to Manchester in 1868 and join the Manchester City Police in early 1869. Furthermore, he was intellectually competent, having been educated in a glorified hedge school. This was much more than thousands of Englishmen could boast of in those days. Illiteracy was very prevalent in the England of those days.

Edward Maxwell's police career came to an abrupt, but as I have discovered, temporary halt towards the end of 1869 due to a set of circumstances that were not of his making. It was only less than two years earlier that the Manchester Martyrs were hanged publicly. This caused great enmity between the Manchester Irish and their English counterparts. It wasn't just the hanging that got to the Irish, it was the crude manner in which the hangman named Colcroft, did his job.

Immediately after the hanging it was discovered that Larkin and O'Brien were still very much alive. It was at this stage that the man employed to do the "job" finished it off with a lump hammer. An enquiry into his butchery was turned down. This callous attitude towards their countrymen led to numerous fights between the Irish and the misguided Englishmen.

It was on being called to a public house to quell one such fight that Edward Maxwell's blood came to an Irish boil. His brother James Maxwell was being set upon by four or more Englishmen and seemed much the worse of this conflict. Edward "stacked" his tunic and got stuck in beside his brother and together with a relation called Charles Sampey from Buckhill, Fairymount, they cleared the pub. It looked like the end of Edward's police career.

I have on my desk documents to prove that it was very far from the end of this famine-stricken man's police career. After much research, I discovered that he joined the Staffordshire Police on the 20th September 1869 and retired 1st January 1896 on a pension. I note that it was in 1869 that he was dismissed from the Manchester Police.

Edward lived out his retirement at the old home in Runnabehy. Cancer claimed him in the end. He now lies sleeping in Glasnevin Cemetery, Dublin awaiting the angel's trumpet. So ends this strange story of a man who seemed, at least for much of his life, unbeatable. May his soul rest in peace.

Actually, he was my great uncle.

The wandering soul of Irish music

IF YOU ARE a youngster who is aspiring to become involved in Irish cultural traditions, you should read this moving story. It is the true story of one of many townlands throughout Ireland's rural countryside, which 150 years ago, captured "the wandering soul of Irish traditional music".

This townland is called Sheepwalk and situated about two miles west of Frenchpark, close to what was once the home of a very great Irishman, Dr Douglas Hyde, the first President of the Republic of Ireland. Today it is a rather peaceful area, sparsely populated with a friendly and generous people.

The last time that I walked along its narrow winding road, it was on a harvest night. A cloudless moon illuminated its lush pasture fields. The only sounds which broke the silence were that of a lowing cow, which apparently had been separated from her offspring. However, Sheepwalk wasn't always like that. In the far off days it was part of the beautiful Lord de Frayne Estate. The majority of its men folk worked at the "Big House" and in addition to their well cultivated plots of land, eked out an honest living.

Until about the year 1840 the only musical sounds within this peaceful setting were that of the birds, apart from - if one could call it musical - the "Big House" bell, as it summoned them to their daily toil. Then one night the "soul of music" wandered into them in the person of a fiddle player from the County Sligo, called Michael Byron. It wasn't very long until the latent talent of Sheepwalk began to surface, as Michael commenced to pass on his skills within their hospitable kitchens.

Michael married a local girl whose family was showing signs of great musical talent and almost a score of years passed before the real musical Sheepwalk began to emerge. In those far off days, youngsters were not permitted to learn music until their schooling had ended, which was about fifteen. However, the Sheepwalk lads were having none of that. They bought themselves penny whistles and led by "Mike" Byron junior, they used to conceal themselves beneath a thick hawthorn outside of the "session house" and gently finger out the melodious notes as they floated fairy-like from within.

When the older generation first discovered their daring plan, they were not very pleased. But after they'd heard them play, so alarmed were they at the high standard achieved by their youngsters in such unusual circumstances, it was decided there and then to start a tin whistle class. The class grew from strength to strength. Then one night somebody came in with the idea of starting a fife and drum band.

At first it all seemed a great big joke: where was the money going to come from? - especially in those days when even pennies were very scarce. Somebody else suggested to approach "His Lordship". The Baron being a musical man himself, decided to support the venture. In a matter of weeks drums, fifes and "what have you" arrived in Sheepwalk.

In the course of time under the expert leadership of a man called John Rourke, the Sheepwalk Fife and Drum Band was to be seen at most social functions throughout the west of Ireland and beyond.

Despite my deepest research, I've been unable to find out the exact name of all the members of that unique band. There were names like the Hopkins brothers, Andrew, Patrick and Tom; Andrew and Thomas Peyton; John and Ned Murray; the Brennan brothers; the Concannon brothers; fife players Patrick Rourke, Patrick Byron, Pat Hopkins and Bernard Beirne, drummer.

However, the bandmaster John Rourke's premature death was a severe blow to the band. His brother Patrick took control and proved to be a very successful leader in the many years that followed.

They say that the soul of music is never content for very long in one particular place and it was only natural that it would fan out in all directions from the historic townland of Sheepwalk. Many of its musicians emigrated. In order to trace the path of its soul, I would have to organise a "Round the World in Eighty Days" trip. However, it did find its way back to Sheepwalk again after an absence of fifty years, when a son of Mike Byron's arrived from the USA with his set of pipes and aroused the ghosts of the past.

One place nearer home, where it did linger for quite a long time is a remarkable townland called Mantuar. It is situated about two miles east of Frenchpark. It has a large tract of fertile land and is surrounded by a vast expanse of virgin bog. Like all Irish townlands, it was once thickly populated; today it is down to a trickle. Inter-marriages between Sheepwalk and Mantuar planted the seeds of culture there, when a sister of the famous fiddle player, Sheepwalk's Tom Tansey, married a man called Pat Casserly of Mantuar. She introduced the fiddle to its hospitable people and in the course of a couple of decades the very versatile people of that remote townland had amazed the countryside by their remarkable achievements.

Pat and Bridget Casserly produced one of the most musical families of the period. There was Pat Junior, a fine fiddle player who emigrated to USA about eighty years ago and later made some recordings there. There was their daughter Mary who settled for the concertina. She married a Sheepwalk man, Mick Mullany. I had the pleasure of hearing her play about sixty years ago; she was brilliant. Another sister Bridget, who married a man called Farrell in the Drumsna-Boyle area, was a wonderful fiddle player. The youngest of the family Bernie was also a good fiddle player. He taught the late Tom Hester of Cloonshanville, who also was a very "sweet" player and a wonderful character. It is said that at one time there was as many as fourteen musicians in this little "Shangri-La". From Mantuar, the magical notes found their way over a wide area of Ballinameen, Croghan and Boyle. However, that is another long and interesting story.

The last remaining link with the great Mantuar tradition, is a man called Thomas Pat McGrath, who is himself a fiddle player and a great cultural historian. Were it not for his valuable research contribution, this unique story could not be told. It was men of his genius and love of everything Irish who, in the past, instilled the spirit of traditional culture into Ireland's youth.

Today many young people are struggling on without that all important "spirit". They seem to be there for the sheer novelty of it. Like a flower in a vase, when the novelty wears off, the talent fades. The history of a song or tune creates a deeper love in the heart of the artiste and where there is love everything is possible.

I wish to dedicate this story to the memory of my late (Sheepwalk born) wife Kathleen, who was a noted traditional singer (R.I.P.).

Fairytales

Before the tragedy of the mid-nineteenth century famine, there was a period of full and plenty throughout the length and breadth of Ireland. The Irish were at that time the best fed people in the whole of Europe, despite the fact that their then population was in the region of eight million. They were also a God fearing people with a firm belief in the "power of prayer" and an unwavering devotion to Mary the Mother of God.

However, the Irish did not confine themselves solely to their religious beliefs. They retained much of their pagan customs despite the great gift of Christianity which they were favoured with from almost the dawn of that era. Even to this very day, many of their superstitions have survived, particularly in the rural areas.

Their established beliefs in the existence of the fairies was indeed rife during the period I've just mentioned. The traditional fairytale was a must in every ramblin' house until television arrived on the scene and rudely interrupted one of many very entertaining pastimes.

There is one particular fairytale which has left an indelible imprint upon my ageing mind - the story of Tom and Nora Vasey and Mave and her Magic Ring.

Mave of the magic ring

IT HAPPENED IN a remote townland near the Sligo border in the summer of 1840. Tom and Nora Vasey were in their late thirties at the time. They lived in a neat rose-covered cottage. A short distance away was a large and unusual "fairy fort". It was surrounded by a huge close-knit blackthorn hedge. Entrance to this fort could only be achieved by forcing your way through a narrow passage between two large rocks. Strangely enough, neither Tom or Nora Vasey ever attempted this hair-raising venture.

One day the local handywoman (midwife) Bessie Sampey called on Nora Vasey for the usual neighbourly chat. Bessie had noticed that Nora was starting to show signs of pregnancy and it being her duty to keep in touch with all the young women of the area, she could not be accused of prying. It later transpired that Bessie's observations were indeed correct. Four months after that friendly visit, Bessie delivered a bouncing baby boy to Tom and Nora.

There was great rejoicing at the Christening of young Vasey. In those days the service was held in the home. He was named after his father, but in order to avoid confusion his mother insisted on calling him Junior. Junior grew, went from strength to strength and at the tender age of nine months he was an exceptionally handsome child, which may have contributed to his experience with the little people.

One fine morning at the crack of dawn Nora heard a strange purring noise circulating around their cottage. She rushed out of bed and crossed the room towards the cot where Junior slept. Her screams soon woke Tom who joined her almost immediately. They both stared spellbound at the blood curdling sight that met their eyes. Instead of the lovely smiling face of their "little jewel" as they affectionately called Junior, they found themselves staring unbelievingly at a disfigured-looking thing with the weathered face of a very old man.

Tom Vasey was a calm collective type of man. After he'd partly recovered from the initial shock he tried unsuccessfully to calm his now hysterical wife.

'I must go and fetch Bessie Sampey right away,' he said, placing a reassuring hand upon Nora's shoulder.

Bessie listened attentively to every word Tom said.

'I must go to your house right away and see for myself' said Bessie, shaking her head despairingly. Nora Vasey stood wailing by the cot which now contained the replacement of her only child. Bessie realised instantly what had happened.

'The "good people", not the bad ones, have taken your child,' and she paused... 'Be calm. There is still great hope.'

Facing Tom Vasey the handywoman took his hand in hers and said in a stern tone of voice,

'As soon as you've had your breakfast you must hit the road immediately in the direction of the Curlews in the County Sligo. There, in a remote corner you'll find a saintly woman they call "Mave of the Magic Ring". If she can't help you there's nobody else can,' concluded Bessie.

Tom Vasey set out upon his sad and weary journey. The Irish had not invented the motor car in those days so Tom had to travel by the only mode available which was Shanks' Mare. He stopped in Boyle town for a quick pint, which cost him tuppence and then faced the long, winding, hilly road which led to the Curlews.

The setting sun was causing the white clouds on the horizon to blush as he approached a large whitethorn hedge at the bend in the road. There, an old man was unsuccessfully trying to extricate a sheep which had got itself entangled in the bushes. Tom went immediately to the old man's assistance and between them they soon extricated the animal without much difficulty. Tom then asked the old man if he could direct him to the place where Mave of the Magic Ring lived.

'You must be in serious trouble my poor man, when 'tis her you seek,' said the old man.

'Serious trouble is right,' replied Tom.

'Come into my house and we'll talk it over while you eat some oat cake and drink fresh milk,' said the old man.

In the course of the meal the old man told him:

'You must continue along the road you've just come for about a quarter of a mile when you'll reach a narrow green boreen on your left. Walk down that boreen for a distance of about two hundred yards till you reach a high stone wall which you must cross. But you must be more than careful when getting down the other side because there is a very steep fall. Should you happen to slip and fall you would be crushed to bits on the huge rocks below.'

'When you get as far as the rocks,' continued the old man, 'you'll notice a very steep incline on your right. Climb to the very top. When you reach the top you'll see a large clump of trees in the distance. You must walk very carefully in the direction of the clump of trees because to the left of the beaten path there's a gaping hole between the rocks called "The Death Trap". As soon as you reach the entry into the tree clump, continue along the path until you come upon another stone wall. Climb carefully over it. After, you'll find a tiny sloping field to your right. At the bottom you'll see a very neat ivy-clad cottage. There lives Mave of the Magic Ring.'

'But,' concluded the old man, 'as you approach the house be careful because Mave has a huge black savage of a dog.'

A couple of hours later, with a golden moon aided by the Milky Way, Tom Vasey found himself approaching the fairy-like ivy-clad cottage. Remembering what the old man had told him about the dog, he moved cautiously. Suddenly a dark figure of an animal darted from the undergrowth and blocked his path. Right there in front of him stood the biggest goat he'd ever seen, its enormous horns glittering in the pale moon's light!

41

Nervously, Tom walked up to the tiny red-painted door and tapped gently. The door creaked melodiously as it partly opened revealing a tall, slim, pleasant-looking woman about in her mid forties.

'Welcome stranger,' said the woman in a very pleasant tone of voice.

'Thank you very kindly,' replied Tom.

'I think I see your trouble in your worried look,' said the woman. 'I am the one you seek. Step inside my humble kitchen.'

Tom Vasey stepped into what he many years after described as "the most heavenly place he'd ever laid foot in". From underneath a long oak table on his left came the unfriendly growl of a dog.

'Calm down Prince,' said the stern voice of Mave of the Magic Ring. The dog immediately obeyed, except for the occasional groan.

'You've come a long way poor man and you certainly must be hungry,' said the woman.

'I am indeed,' replied Tom.

'Take a seat my good man. We'll eat first then we'll start talking,' said the hospitable woman.

While Mave was preparing the meal, Tom viewed the fairy-like kitchen with sincere admiration. The walls were immaculately white. The tiny dresser was of black oak and of excellent workmanship. It was profusely ornamented with various designs of delph of the extremely antique type. The mantelpiece was apparently the work of the same hand, above which hung an unusual picture of the thorn-crowned Christ. On the right was a picture of His mother and in the centre a picture of the Irish national saint, Patrick. A tiny turf fire glowed invitingly upon the hearth as crickets sang sharply within the dark polished hob.

After a hearty meal of home-cured bacon fried with ducks' eggs, they both faced one another across the fire for - well, for what Tom had come for. After a pause Mave asked,

'Is it a boy?'

She knew!

'It is indeed,' replied Tom, astounded.

'What age is he?'

'Just nine months and a few days,' answered Tom nervously.

'Oh, I'm delighted you've said that,' said Mave cheerfully. 'It is much easier to get a child of that age back than say, one of two or three years.'

Mave glanced at the small clock on the oak dresser. She then smiled and looked triumphantly into the eyes of the worried man who'd just lost his darling boy.

'In a few minutes you and I will be going for a walk,' she said. 'Listen carefully to what I've got to say Tom. You're to keep a distance behind me and on no account are you to speak, unless spoken to by me. Should you hear a voice or voices other than mine, keep absolutely silent. So, now let us go.'

Slowly Mave led Tom to the left of the house, then along a mossy path sheltered by two holly hedges. At the end of this path was a high embankment from which a huge rock protruded. Here the hedges ended revealing a romantic full moon. Mave then climbed cautiously up the steps which led to the top of the huge rock, removed a large gold ring from her skirt pocket, faced the yellow moon, placed the ring in front of her eyes and spoke some words which Tom couldn't catch. A voice to the rear of Tom asked in a sharp tone,

'Are you satisfied with the arrangement, Vasey?' Tom placed his hand upon his mouth and remained silent.

Then from the rock came the voice of Mave.

'Is your wife tall, slim with brown hair, Tom Vasey?'

'That is correct,' said Tom.

'I see a much older woman with greying hair parted in the middle.'

'That is the handywoman who acts as midwife in our part of the country,' replied Tom.

'Has your boy rosy cheeks, brown hair and hazel eyes?'

'That's him. As sure as God that's him,' cried Tom.

Mave put the ring back in her pocket, came slowly down from the rock and placing her hand gently upon Tom's shoulder she said,

'Your darling boy has just been returned to his cot. Thank God it was the "good people" that had him, or else I'd not be able to help.'

An Irish emigrant
and his dog

A ROMANTIC SUMMER moon, aided by numerous stars, illuminated the Roscommon/Sligo border as Barney O'Toole made his way across the lush pasture field in the direction of his home. Away to his right he could see the tiny churchyard on the hill where generations of his people, including his beloved parents and childhood sweetheart, lay awaiting the sound of the angel's trumpet.

Barney had just taken his faithful sheepdog Bob to his best friend and neighbour Mattie O'Connor to care for it during whatever period he would remain in England. He was naturally lonely at having to part with Bob in this manner. However, he was very much consoled by the fact that Mattie and Bob were the best of friends and besides, Mattie's wife Mave was exceptionally fond of all animals.

B arney crossed over the old stone stile and into the meadow field adjacent his home. He walked slowly along the path until he came to the lone oak on his left. This giant tree had been planted by his grandfather even before his father's time. He recalled how he and his late father used to shelter beneath its sturdy branches whenever they decided to have a short break from their daily toil.

There were those days when as a child he sat beneath this same tree and watched his dad swing the old scythe to and fro. He imagined he could hear the musical sounds of the blade as his father expertly guided the blue scythe-stone along its sides. In addition, there was the humming of the bees as they plied their scientific trade of extracting honey from the wild flowers.

The door of his neatly kept, rose-covered cottage creaked faintly as Barney pushed it open. He switched on the electric light and cast a slow glance all around the old farmhouse kitchen with its antique furniture. The crickets were singing sharply within the old black-polished hob. He'd heard his late mother say,

'Whenever the crickets sing sharply 'tis a sign of rain.' The antique clock which hung above the fireplace chimed twelve as Barney damped the fire and retired for the night.

Next morning Barney awoke to the ever familiar sounds associated with an Irish mid-June rural scene. Cattle were lowing in the distant pasture field, sheep were bleating plaintively within the Baron's estate. The early skylarks were chanting their crisp and melodious notes in flawless unison. Down by the gurgling trout stream nature's ventriloquists, the corncrakes, were casting their familiar croaky voices in expertly chosen directions. On the ash outside of Barney's bedroom window, a lone cuckoo was delivering its over-repeated oration in its changed tone of voice. The shrill crowing of a neighbour's cock re-echoed amid the distant hills.

The early morning sun was peeping through Barney's open bedroom window. In the distance he could plainly see "Ben Bulben" as it towered majestically above the fairy-like beauty of beloved County Sligo, at the same time watching guard over that hallowed spot which will for all time clasp to its bosom the immortal remains of William Butler Yeats. A silver curtain of mist hung lazily above that spot, then, aided by a gentle June breeze, drifted slowly out to sea.

Barney slid lazily out of bed, dressed casually and made his way towards the kitchen. The few sods he'd left close to the fire the night before were pepper-dry. There was little difficulty in starting a fire. He got himself some tea and toast, but this particular morning he did not feel like eating. He was leaving his once happy home where, being the only child of Jack and Mary O'Toole he'd always been treated like a prince. Now he was almost ready to leave it for apparently the same reasons that countless Irishmen and women before him had done. Things might have been different had his childhood sweetheart Katie Raftery not been taken in the flower of her youth with that then dreaded disease tuberculosis.

Barney finished dressing as slowly as he could, took one last long look at the photo of his parents which hung above the mantelpiece in an oval frame, picked up his case which had been packed the night before and went smartly outside. There was no need to lock up, he thought. He'd arranged with Mattie O'Connor to look after things and besides, he'd let the land to Mattie. Taking one long mournful look at his home and surroundings, Barney O'Toole walked briskly up the old mossy boreen in the direction of the public road.

He'd only gone a short distance when a brown squirrel frisked nimbly across his path, climbed briskly on to a lower branch of a blooming hawthorn and commenced to wash its cheeky face with its tiny paws. Before reaching the bend in the boreen, Barney turned around and took his last look at the old homestead. After he'd rounded the bend a close blackthorn hedge hid his home surroundings from view.

With tear-filled eyes he walked briskly on. He thought he heard a noise at the back of the hedge on his left and after he'd gone a few more paces, Bob came dashing through an opening in the hedge and commenced to jump with joy in front of his master. Bob trotted on in front of Barney 'till they both reached the public road. Then the faithful friend faced Barney and stared questioningly for a brief few seconds. Releasing a prolonged wail the dog turned and raced off in the direction of the O'Connors' home.

Barney O'Toole was too upset after the encounter with Bob that he almost failed to notice the familiar rabbit warren on his right as he walked along the deserted country road. The warren was a high mound which was covered with a thick coat of shrubbery. Countless animals darted in and out of their shelters and gazed in turn at the sight of the man with the suitcase in his hand.

Further on and to his right was the Baron's deer park. It was surrounded by a high stone wall that had been built a couple of hundred years before, when labour was costing about fourpence a day. A large herd of deer was grazing peacefully in the centre of the park. Away to the right of the herd was a huge buck, its antlers like the branches of a divested tree on a bleak November day.

About two hundred yards further on was a "fairy fort". Its three circular rings adorned with blooming hawthorn gave it the appearance of a giant's wedding cake. There were numerous birds incubating their eggs within this fairy sanctuary. A large fox emerged from the entrance to its cave which wormed its way beneath the three rings. The fox stared cunningly at Barney for a split second then darted swiftly in the direction of a nearby wood.

Immediately after rounding the hairpin bend Barney had reached the main bus route. He stood in silence for a minute or so, then put down his case and commenced to ponder. For a brief few minutes he got the urge to go back, after all, some of his neighbours had holdings that were even smaller than his and they were getting on, well, struggling on. He glanced to his left and spotted the bus approaching. Barney flagged it down. The huge green monster ground to a halt. He picked up the case and boarded the bus. In a matter of seconds Barney O'Toole was speeding away from his once happy home and his faithful friend Bob.

Eighteen months later it was Christmas Eve. A car ground to a halt on the snow-covered road in front of the boreen which led to Barney O'Toole's home. All its four windows were brilliantly illuminated. Mattie O'Connor and his wife were busy all that day preparing for the home-coming of Barney O'Toole and his Irish bride Grace. After Barney had settled with the hackney driver and retrieved the cases from the boot of the car, himself and Grace commenced to walk firmly down the old boreen in the direction of Barney's house. They had only gone a short distance when they heard the clattering of paws in the snow. Bob dashed towards his long lost master and commenced leaping for joy. Barney clasped Bob in his arms while Grace patted the friendly dog's head.

The O'Tooles were home to stay.

Rat race to a
stately mansion

*"I picked up an old broom and with one swipe, the Duke of Westminster's
wealth was reduced by a single rat".*

THIS STORY BEGAN in the early hours of a pleasant May morning in
1937. The Holyhead boat train came to a halt at Chester railway station. I
jumped to my feet, got hold of the old suitcase which I had inherited from a
great-uncle and leapt lightly on to the platform. I felt lost in the unusual
surroundings, as my tired eyes scanned the faces of rank strangers.

My brother John came striding towards me. After we'd exchanged
greetings John ushered me towards the exit, then along a dark street, eventually ending up in a house in Victor Street, which was owned by an Irish
Landlady. John had stayed there the previous night in anticipation of my
arrival. The crackling of bacon and sausage in the large pan was music to my
ears.

After breakfast, we both set out on foot to the farm where John worked. It was at a village called Allford and about five miles from Chester. The bus service didn't start till 8 a.m. and John was due to start work at 6.30 a.m. His boss kept a large herd of cows. He also bred race horses and won the Grand National on one occasion, with a horse called Russian Hero. It was ridden by an Irish jockey called Pat Sweeney.

By the time we'd reached this farm place, "the merry sounds of mirth and labour" had commenced. After we'd ascended a long step-ladder, I found myself inside my first "Paddy Shant". The odious smell which came from about a dozen calves, housed right underneath the "Shant" was, to say the least, extremely off-putting. John got into his work outfit while I surveyed his "home from home". Furniture was indeed very scanty. It consisted of a fairly decent bed, two chairs and a small table.

I rolled into bed and lay there pondering on the home I'd left and also wondering what kind of "Paddy Shant" I'd end up in. The lowing of the hungry calves downstairs was a complete obstruction to sleep. Two hours later, John entered by the narrow door carrying a large jug filled with tea and a tiny basket filled with bacon sandwiches. After we'd breakfasted for the second time that morning I decided to go in search of a job.

I retraced my steps back along the Chester Road, calling to every farm along the way. Would you believe, I got the identical reply from each farmer I asked!

'Sorry, filled up Paddy.'

I eventually came to a country public house called "The Rake and Pikle". I entered this pub by the back way, which was something I'd been in the habit of doing over in my native Roscommon.

I was amazed when the friendly landlord of The Rake and Pikle asked me:

'Did you come over last night Paddy?'

The message this question conveyed to me was: "you look very green in my eyes". While I gulped down my first pint of English beer, the landlord kept phoning the farm places in the area, in an effort to find me a job. I learned later that this public house was called "Paddy's Exchange".

Before I left, he informed me that I could find a job at a farm in a village called Churton, which lies between Chester and Wrexham and about two miles from the farm where my brother John worked. I got a bus ride back to Allford and dropped off at the end of the drive which led to the farm where we'd both arrived earlier that morning.

As directed by my landlord friend, I called next evening to the Churton farm.

Yes of course, he'd remembered the phone call.

'You can start in the morning,' he added. He then pointed out an old shabby-looking wooden hut in the stackyard. 'That's where you'll be staying with two of your own countrymen,' he added. 'I do hope you'll prove to be satisfactory,' he concluded.

I knocked gently upon the battered black door. A very pronounced Irish accent came from within.

'Come in, if you're Irish and good-looking.' I pushed the door open. It creaked musically, then wedged solid against the floor. In the dim light which struggled through a dirty, small window, I spotted two figures seated by a long table, apparently enjoying their evening meal. A huge rat darted past me, then made good its escape through the narrow doorway. This was but a "curtain-raiser" of things to come.

I quickly learned that my two Irish and future companions were from a place called Dunmore in the County Galway. One was in his early fifties and called Pat. The other was in his early sixties and called Jim. After they'd treated me to a "jampot" of tea, some bread, butter and cold ham, we commenced to chat. In the course of our conversation I asked,

'Do you have many rats in here? I just met one on the way out, as I came in.'

'Plenty,' replied Jim, adding 'The one you met is gone to tell the others that you've arrived.'

Glancing towards the roof, I spotted two large shopping bags. They were suspended from the rafters by means of wire rope. This strange arrangement rather puzzled me. I was about to ask a silly question when "the penny dropped".

'Is it really all that bad?' I asked. Nodding in the direction of the shopping bags.

'I see you're beginning to learn Bernard,' replied Jim, as he burst out into a hearty Irish laugh.

Pat jumped to his feet.

'Come with me Bernard, till I try and find you the makin' of a "Paddy Shant bed" .' He took me down the yard to a barn where the cow-feed was stored. There, he sorted out five large empty sacks. Passing the sacks on to me he said,

'There's your sheets and blankets for starters.' He then took me to a large shed where the machinery was kept. There he picked up a small camp bed frame. We returned to the hut and erected a third bed in a rat-infested environment.

Before retiring that night, Jim gave me some very sound, if far from encouraging advice.

'If you happen to be bitten by a rat or two tonight Bernard, consider yourself honoured.'

'Why?' I asked.

'Well you see,' said he, 'everything for miles around here belongs to the Duke of Westminster, so it must be an honour to be bitten by a Royal Rat.'

I wasn't convinced!

I scrambled into what passed for a bed and prayed more fervently than ever before, that it would not happen. From sheer exhaustion I dropped off to sleep almost immediately. Jim's loud snoring woke me up just about day-break. To my immense horror and without exaggeration, there were three rats surveying my sack covering, while another was gently nibbling at my left ear. I was young and agile in those days. I must have jumped about five feet high, from beneath my English blankets!

The Galway men were out of their beds almost immediately. Pat made his way to the door and switched the light on. In the dim lighting I saw two large rats leap from the table, while another was expertly descending towards the shopping bag. I picked up an old broom and with one swipe, the Duke of Westminster's wealth was reduced by one well fed rat…

The long fine summer drifted into harvest. It was approaching the Duke of Westminster's annual harvest festival, which was invariably held at Eton Hall near Chester, the Duke's Stately mansion. One evening, while strolling in the direction of the local pub called "The White Horse", it dawned on me that if I should be honoured to be bitten by the Duke's rats, I should also be entitled to an invitation to his harvest festival.

I usually frequented the "taproom" of The White Horse. On this occasion I was tempted to go into the lounge where the employees from Lady Mary's place used to go. Lady Mary was the daughter of the Duke. She lived in a stately home in the village of Churton. Rumour had it that she was in fact a man-hater, on account of the old Duke's lifestyle.

As I went into the lounge, I noticed a very aristocratic-looking man of middle age, greying hair and a well trained moustache. He was engrossed in a paper called "The Chester Chronicle". I walked to the counter and ordered a pint of bitter. The landlord looked at me askance; I returned the compliment. However, he did serve me and I took up my position in a corner opposite this gentleman.

He folded his paper and placed it on the table in front of him and then stared questioningly in my direction.

'Good evening, stranger,' he said. 'You don't come from these parts I gather.'

'Good evening, kindly sir,' I replied. 'In fact I do come from these parts. I live and work in Churton.' I then related to him, not just the place and nature of my employment, but also the story of the rats.

'Good gracious old boy, you don't mean to tell me you were bitten by rats,' he exclaimed excitedly. I assured him it was indeed, positively true.

'I say old boy, I do a bit of writing, do you mind if I use this alarming story about this damn rat affair?'

'Not in the least,' I replied.

'Can I use your name and address?' he asked.

'Of course you can,' I replied. While he was entering my name and address in his notebook, my mind was working overtime.

'Do you mind if I ask you a question Mr...'

'Shankley's the name,' he cut in.

'If I should be obliged to be honoured by being bitten by the Duke's rats, should I be honoured with an invitation to his harvest festival?'

'You're jolly well right, old boy,' he said, adding, 'leave it with me.'

Four days later, while I was washing the milking machines, the farmer approached me and handed me a very official-looking letter. It was an invitation to the Duke of Westminster's harvest festival! Pat and Jim had left the place a few weeks earlier, or they too might have been invited. The festival itself is the makings of another interesting story.

Drama and romance on
"The Rocks"

A SPRINKLING OF snowflakes were descending like butterflies upon the old boreen as Connie Gray, Katie Lee and Vera Lynch made their way in the direction of the lake. They were invited to a party to be held in Sheila Forde's home on the peninsula. Sheila had returned to her parents' home to spend the Christmas. Katie and Vera were related to the Forde family and Connie was a noted flute player.

Connie and Katie had been lovers ever since their school days, that was until John Lee decided that Katie should marry a wealthy farmer known locally as "The Jobber". Katie partly consented to the suggestion at first but later asked for a stay of three months to consider this very important venture. This meant that the frosty relationship between Connie and Katie fitted in with the atmospheric conditions of the night of the party.

As they reached the lake shore, the lights from the Fordes' windows were so prominent that the mile distance across to the peninsula only seemed a few hundred yards away. The old tin can in the bottom of the boat reflected the moon's light as it emerged from behind a snow curtain. Connie entered the boat known as "The Cockle" because of its unusual small size and started to teem the water, which had seeped in over the week, overboard.

To the left of the peninsula lay a treacherous island called "The Rocks". Suddenly there came the lonely wail of a number of swans in The Rocks area. Vera Lynch became greatly alarmed at this sudden lament and decided there and then not to cross over to the peninsula. Her old grandmother had so often told her to pay heed to the swans' warning, especially since the three poteen makers were drown returning from the island with their booty.

Connie brushed Vera's story aside as "a load of old grannies' superstition" and asked Katie if she too wanted to turn back. After a prolonged pause Katie replied,

'Wherever you go Connie, I'm prepared to follow!' Connie thought for a few moments and wondered if Katie's reply had deeper significance than just crossing to the peninsula. Vera apologised and wished them both luck, then started back up the boreen in the direction of home.

Katie struggled aboard. Connie then pushed The Cockle away from the shore, entered the boat and grabbed the oars with his back to the peninsula. Katie sat facing the peninsula. Katie's task was to warn Connie should he start to go off course.

Over on the peninsula Forde's front door opened. The rhythm of céilí music from a blend of instruments seemed to warm the chill night air. It faded just as quickly with the closing of the door. This was indeed a wonderful boost to the pair of ex-lovers in The Cockle as it skimmed gracefully over the calm water. Just then the moon dropped behind a distant mountain as a wintry fog seemed to gradually emerge from nowhere. Katie warned Connie that Forde's lights seemed to be getting dimmer.

The fog got denser. The lights disappeared altogether and worse still, the swans' lament which served as a warning as to where The Rocks lay, suddenly ceased. The sound of music returned briefly, it warned both of them that they were slightly veering east and off course. Katie shivered gently at the thought of what Vera had said about the swans' warning. She wondered if Vera had done the right thing after all. Connie raised the oars and let The Cockle drift for a few brief moments. He then decided to alter course while Katie took a torch from her handbag and commenced to flash distress signals.

The swans again resumed their plaintive cries and it was clear that they had changed their venue. Their lonely wails came from an island south of The Rocks called Bawn. This strange omen had a very demoralising effect on Connie as well as on Katie. Again, Connie raised the oars and allowed The Cockle to drift aimlessly in the now inky blackness. Katie suggested shouting for help but Connie's pride overruled her.

'Don't worry darling,' he assured her. 'We'll soon be there.' Katie pulled her cloak tight about her and offered a silent prayer.

Connie thought he caught a glimpse of Forde's lights. He dropped the oars and commenced to pull with all his might. The Cockle skimmed over the smooth lake like an overgrown swan. Suddenly Katie let out a prolonged scream.

'Connie! Connie!' she shouted, pointing in the direction in which The Cockle was heading. 'A phantom boat with three men aboard. It's just crossed our path and then disappeared!'

'Nonsense,' replied Connie. 'It's all in your imagination. You've been carried away by Vera's silly story.'

'No! no!' pleaded Katie. 'I tell you it's real and what's more they didn't have oars!' Connie did not reply but kept on rowing.

Once again the music from Forde's house sounded clear. It really served as a warning this time, that they were indeed away off course of the peninsula and heading close to The Rocks. Katie covered her face with her scarf while Connie tried to slow down by dropping the oars deep into the water, but he was far too late for that now. There was a violent crash. The tiny craft was lifted clean out of the water. With the crackling sounds of breaking wood it came to a halt upon a submerged bed of rock, its bottom torn apart.

Connie lost his grip on the oars but managed to hold onto the seat. Katie was catapulted from her seat in the end of the boat and finished up in Connie's arms. She then passed out. The water by this time reached a dangerous level inside the boat. Connie struggled to his feet still holding Katie in his aching arms. He was almost knee-deep in water. Tightly holding onto Katie he tried to find his bearings. He wasn't quite sure if the boat was pointing in the direction of the island or if it foundered obliquely. He knew from his daylight experience of the surroundings, that to move in the wrong direction would mean them both walking into instant death. Neither of them could swim.

Where was Katie's torch? he asked himself. He thought he remembered her putting it in her handbag shortly before the crash. The fog had lifted slightly. He looked into the pleasant features of the girl he held in his arms and he thought too of the wealthy "Jobber". He shook Katie violently and called her name. Katie raised a gloved hand and grasped at the thin December air.

'Are you...alright...Connie?' she whispered.

'Of course I'm alright,' he replied, as he kissed her frozen lips. 'The torch, Katie! Where's the torch?' She pointed to her cloak. Connie found the torch and flashed it in the direction he believed The Rocks lay. To his utter dismay there was no sign of its giant boulders. He tried the opposite direction. The evil looking island loomed large about thirty yards distant. Katie had by this time recovered sufficiently to stand on her own feet. With arms around each other, they waded through varying depths of icy water until eventually they found themselves on dry, rocky ground.

The inside of the large cave was both crude and black. It was for many years the "home" of poteen distillers. There was a large fireplace with a funnel leading through the stone flagged roof. Two large sacks of turf were stacked to one side. A tin drum containing water was in the centre. A few tin mugs and an old biscuit tin which contained a mixture of tea and sugar, together with an old tin kettle, gave a touch of civilisation to the primitive interior of the cave. Katie found a half box of "Friendly" matches inside one of the sacks of turf.

With the light from the torch Connie and Katie started to get a fire going. In less than twenty minutes the leaping flames illuminated the weird surroundings. They discarded their wet clothing and placed it in front of the multi-coloured flames to dry. Connie sat near the cave entrance periodically flashing distress signals in the direction of the mainland, while Katie dried their wet clothing and brewed black tea in the old tin kettle.

At the first touch of dawn a motor boat was heading in the direction of The Rocks, a Gardai patrol having spotted Connie's distress signals. Connie and Katie, lovers that they were forever, stood hand in hand high up on a boulder to warn the patrol of the whereabouts of the submerged rocks.

The dual secret

It was a glorious harvest day in 1935. A Crossley coach sped peacefully along the road that links Chester to Wrexham. It came to a halt in front of The White Horse Inn which is the only public house in the historic village of Churton. A tall, slim man in his late sixties stepped from the coach carrying a large black leather suitcase. He paused for a minute or so to survey the pleasant surroundings, then walked slowly across the road and entered the pub.

The spacious tap room was almost empty except for a few old-timers who were sat in a quiet corner. They were drinking from earthen mugs (it was the custom amongst old men in those days). The innkeeper emerged from a back room, eyed the stranger questioningly, then asked if he could help him.

'Gee, I'm hoping you can,' replied the stranger. 'First of all I'd love to sample your beer. Then I'd be grateful if you'll tell me about the cottage down the old cul-de-sac. I mean is it still there?'

'I'm afraid I can't help you there my friend, actually I've only just taken over this place,' said the Innkeeper.

'I think this is where I can be of help,' came a voice from the corner. 'The cottage to which you refer is still there. However, it is in pretty bad shape at the moment. It's not been inhabited for donkeys' years; not I think since old Sam Holt lived there.' Another old-timer interrupted to say he thought Sam Holt passed it on to a young Irish lad who later emigrated to Australia.

'Well, that's fine,' said the stranger. 'In that case I'd better go along and check it out.' He finished his beer, thanked the innkeeper and his informants, made a quick exit and set out in the direction of the cul-de-sac.

The stranger saw little change in the narrow lane as he walked in the shelter of its hawthorn hedges. The lone defiant oak stood out as bold as ever. He could see the field of ripe corn on his left. It was twittering in a gentle breeze. A herd of cows on his right grazed peacefully.

'They sure are the Duke of Westminster's breed,' he murmured.

He arrived at the cottage. The once neatly kept hedge had grown wild obscuring the lower windows of his "mansion" as he used to call it. The small wooden gate had rotted beyond recognition and when he tried to push it open it simply disintegrated. It made such a crackling sound that half a dozen rabbits scurried in all directions. The rotting door hung precariously upon rusting hinges.

'Gee golly, I sure have my work cut out for me here,' murmured the stranger.

"The stranger" had his cottage newly renovated. He had many visitors in the years that followed. They were mostly Irishmen who worked in the surrounding farm places. His English contemporaries paid him periodic visits as well. They all loved to hear his hair-raising tales of the "wild bush". He'd got the real art of storytelling and besides, his home-distilled poteen was the biggest attraction, although the English found it slightly stronger than what they were used to. Also, a great attraction was the promise that one day he would reveal to them the unique story of his fairytale life.

One day as the festive season of Christmas was approaching, the stranger informed his Churton friends that he was prepared to pay for a real farewell party, if the good people of Churton would find a venue and help him out with the arrangements. They all agreed and an old school-house was chosen as the venue. The stranger then made it known that on the night of the party he was, at long last, going to fulfil his promise by unlocking the door of his secret apartment and reveal to them its alarming contents.

On the party night a piper arrived from Chester in the midst of the hilarious gathering. He'd been invited there by one of the Irish lads who had spent so many enjoyable nights in the hospitable home of the stranger. This was the big night in more ways than one. It was the night on which the long kept secret was about to be revealed, if not to the world, at least to the homely folk of the village of Churton. Every known ruse was attempted in an effort to try and find even the stranger's name - all failed. He even signed himself "The Stranger".

Towards the end of the party, the stranger made his way to the low platform in the corner of the schoolroom. His heavy mop of white hair was in disarray. It was quite obvious that he'd drunk his fill. He stepped onto the stage and raised his right hand. The babel began to fade slowly until complete silence prevailed. In a clear tone of voice, the stranger commenced.

'My dear people of the ancient village of Churton. It gives me much pleasure to see all of you enjoying yourselves immensely. Your friendliness, company and co-operation has added endless joy to my fading years. I really don't know what it was that endeared me to the kind folk of this area, perhaps it was the suspense created by my promise to reveal my inner secrets one day. You still don't know my name even now. All I ever told you was that I spent most of my life in Australia's wild bush.'

'I don't intend to bore you with any of the sordid details of my long life. First of all I'm going to give you as accurate an account as possible of the manner in which I first arrived on this planet, seventy-odd years ago. I shall go on to reveal to you the extraordinary circumstances which revealed to me my true self in the course of life's long weary way. Since I have neither kith or kin I shall now honour the good people of Churton with my unique and as you will find, interesting life story.'

'It was on a cold March morning about the year 1865 that a bunch of lads and lassies returning from a dance somewhere in Ireland heard the cry of an infant within a small garden close to a catholic church. On further investigation they found a male child, wrapped in woollens and inside of a basket. After the police were informed, the baby was christened in the nearby church. Since its parentage could not be found, the youngster had no name. So, they named it Felex Gardener.'

'My earliest recollections are of a large house where a number of children, old people and young girls lived. The place was run by an authoritative woman whom we were allowed to call Mother. We were regularly punished by the elders, sometimes for no apparent reason. In the nearby school, we were invariably isolated from the other children outside of the large house. The only social life that I can recall was during the Christmas season. We were also allowed to parade on Saint Patrick's Day.'

'At the tender age of fourteen years, I was contracted out to a bachelor farmer for the handsome sum of five pounds a year. Life was rough on the farm. The old man was kind though, he did provide me with good clothes and often gave me extra money for spending. This was a secret that had to be kept from his married sister who called regularly to do some chores. It was she who so often told me what I was. It was she who kept reminding me of where I was found on that cold March morning by the folk on their way home from a dance.'

'At the age of twenty-one my contract with the farmer came to an end. In all fairness he did offer to increase my salary, should I desire to stay. But that night at a church function I won three pounds. About a week later I said farewell to the old farmer, put my few things in an old bag and walked the three miles to the nearest railway station. There I purchased a ticket, a single fare to Chester, for six shillings and ninepence.'

'I arrived in Chester on a pleasant May morning in the year 1886. I found work five days later at Church Farm here in Churton. I had many happy nights in The White Horse Inn and also in the little village of Farndon, which as you all know is but two miles from Churton. The pay was pretty good at Church Farm though the hours were very long in those days. I became very friendly with a man who lived in the cottage down the cul-de-sac. He seemed not to have any relatives and before he died he made the cottage over to me. His name was Sam Holt.'

'It was a year later that I decided to try my luck "down under". So, I set out on the long weary journey to partly-unexplored Australia. Shortly after my arrival there I came in contact with a timber merchant, who eventually lured me into becoming a professional lumberjack. I was to spend many lonesome years in wild bush country. We lived in crude huts. Life, to say the least, was rough - but the money was good. I made tucks of cash one way or another!'

'Horses were plentiful in the bush. In fact, they were the only means of transport. Shopping meant a couple of days' journey to the nearest store. We distilled our own whiskey called "hooch". Our slice of the bush was sparsely populated. Social life was non-existent. I devoted much of my time to horse riding, as a hobby of course. It was a pastime which I found to be very rewarding in more ways than one.'

'One evening in late June, I decided to take my horse, the bay, for a canter into the unknown. As darkness descended upon the dense forest, I suddenly found that I'd lost my bearings. There was no alternative only to keep on riding until daylight.'

'Some hours later I found myself in a large opening. This raised my hopes of habitation being close at hand. I trotted the bay round the opening many times in the hope of finding a glimmer of life. It was not unusual to find the odd aborigine living in isolation and what better friend could one find in the wilds of that vast region? There were a number of tracks I could have chosen which led out of the opening. I decided to let "horse sense" take over, which meant letting the bay doddle along and take the first track it stood at.'

'The horse eventually halted near one particular track which seemed rather narrow. I decided to make a go for it but before long discovered that it had got too narrow for comfort. I was just about to abandon it when I spotted a dim light on my right. A fairly wide track led me to a crudely built cabin from which the glimmer of light came. I dismounted, then knocked gently upon a plain unpainted door. There was no response so I knocked a second time.'

'A male voice came from within the cabin,'

' "Who goes there?" it said.'

' "I'm lost! Please can you help me?" There was about a minute's silence.'

' "What is your name?" he asked.'

' "The name's Felex Gardener," I replied.'

' "Fel-ex Gard-ner," he repeated in a surprised tone of voice. The door opened with a crackling sound that frightened the bay. Framed in the doorway stood a medium-sized man. In the dim candlelight it was hard to tell his age.'

' "Step inside young man," he said in a weak kind of voice.'

'A lively log fire burned on an uneven hearth. Puffs of smoke filtered round the ghostly room. A bedstead made of rough timbers stretched along the wall on my left. There were a couple of home-made things to sit upon. A small table and a large dresser, which contained almost every item of household utensil, completed this one-roomed cabin's furnishings. A large hunk of well-smoked bacon hung above the blackened fireplace.'

'After a hearty meal of fried bacon, black home-made bread and plenty of black coffee laced with hooch, we commenced to chat. The old man stared at me long and hard.'

' "Do you mind if I ask you a personal question Felex?" he blurted out.'

' "No, of course not," I replied.'

' "Where on earth did you get such an un-Irish name as Felex Gardener?" he queried. There was a prolonged silence. I looked into the friendly log fire in the hope of finding an answer to his very pointed question. Had he tippled to the kind of stray the old farmer's sister had so often told me I was? I thought. I then turned to my host and asked:'

' "What about yourself? You haven't told me what your name is." He looked sharply into my eyes. Then after a long pause he said in a tender tone of voice:'

' "I think we both have a story to tell about our lives. There might even be a link somewhere along the way." '

' "It seems impossible" I replied.'

'My hospitable host struggled to his feet, then began to pace the earthen floor. He leaned upon the end of the bed and started to speak in low, emotional tones.'

' "My name is John Nann, a bit un-Irish too don't you think?" I nodded in agreement. "I was born of humble parents" he continued. "One night at a church function I became friendly with a charming girl called Julia. It was love at first sight for us both. We were forced to keep our love affair secret because her parents were rich. In the course of the next twelve months we'd many secret meetings." '

' "One night we had planned to meet at our usual rendezvous in order to put the final touches to our secret elopement. We'd both known for a long time that Julia was expecting our baby. This was something we dare not make known to her parents." The old man was now shaking with emotion. He crossed the floor and sat facing me.'

' "Would you like me to continue?" '

' "Of course," I replied.'

' "She failed to turn up for that meeting," he went on. "On my way home I kept repeating to myself 'What on earth has happened to my Julia...?' That night I lay awake pondering. I had a strong feeling that my Julia was indeed in trouble. Next morning the news spread that a male infant was found near to our church." '

'He poured us both another glass of hooch, then went on.'

' "Later that day I had a terrible shock. Julia was admitted to hospital the night before." He paused, then he sighed: "She died shortly after." '

' "Her father was a very influential man!" he shouted.'

' "Do you understand what I'm trying to tell you?" he asked in a voice filled with emotion.'

' "I think I've got the message," I replied.'

' "They christened the baby in our local church and because its parents could not be traced, what do you think they called it?" he asked. There was dead silence for a minute or two. I broke the silence by whispering:'

' "Felex Gardener." '

'Good people of Churton, that is my long kept secret.'

There was prolonged applause. The party went on all night amidst the twirling of Irish pipes.

Gold beneath a hanging tree

THE STRANGER

IT WAS A roasting hot day in June of the early nineteenth century that a little man called Johnny Rush arrived in the quiet town of Frenchpark in the County Roscommon. His only worldly goods were a leather bag which contained his working tools - for Johnny was a joiner by trade - and a penny tin whistle which he had tucked inside his worn jacket pocket. Johnny strolled into the little pub called "Darby's Well", called for a pint of Guinness, then placed his toolkit on the pub floor and started to search in his waistcoat pocket for the two penny coins which was the price of a pint of creamy stuff in those far off, good ould days.

The landlord of Darby's Well happened to be a cantankerous kind of fellow who'd always been very wary of strangers. He eyed Johnny rather suspiciously.

'You're a stranger in these parts I gather?' queried the landlord.

'A stranger is right,' replied Johnny. 'I've only just arrived here.'

'There's a place on the outskirts where you might have a chance of a bed till you sort yourself out,' said the landlord. 'They call the old fellow who lives there "Soldier French". A funny sort,' he added.

Johnny knocked gently on the red-painted door of the three roomed thatched cottage. There was a rumbling noise inside. A few minutes later the red door opened with a nasty creak.

'What do you want stranger?' came the gruff voice of the soldier.

'I'm a stranger right enough,' replied Johnny. 'I called to ask if you'll be kind enough to put me up for a few weeks till I find a little place of my own.'

'How come you called here?' asked Soldier French.

'The landlord of a pub called Darby's Well sent me,' said Johnny.

'You should have told me at the start,' snapped the soldier. 'Well, you'd better be stepping inside and making yourself at home I suppose.'

The local parish priest employed Johnny a few days later to carry out some repair to the church in Frenchpark and after he'd established himself as a perfect joiner, Johnny set about finding a small patch of ground upon which he could build himself a neat hut in which to live. Land was very hard to come by in Frenchpark in those days. The local baron owned all of it, which he let to his over-worked tenants at an exorbitant rent.

One day as Johnny went for a stroll in the nearby woods, he met with the old baron himself who immediately challenged Johnny for trespassing in his wood.

'I'm very sorry your honour,' said Johnny. 'You see my lord,' continued Johnny, 'my story is a sad one.' So he up and told the old baron what had happened to him, ending up by saying that he was on the lookout for a small patch of ground where he could build a little hut for himself.

The old gentleman must have been impressed by Johnny's story for he immediately offered him a site for his hut within a fairy fort* which was situated on the fringe of his vast estate. What Johnny did not know was that the old baron's offer was a big joke for the simple reason that nobody in their sane senses would dare to build on a fairy fort. But what the baron did *not* know was that before leaving his native Mayo, Johnny had a vivid dream

* I once heard a very old man say 'The great tunes of Matt Molloy, Frank Jordan, Sonny Flanagan, Mark Gara and Brian Flynn and many more, had their origin in and around that same fairy fort'. There are those in this day and age of television who brush all this aside as "ould codswallop", but I was born between two of these forts and I believe that they are part of the backdrop to our great culture. B.D.

that he would find his fortune outside his little hut, within a fairy fort in a place called Frenchpark in the County Roscommon.

When the local people heard this they were flabbergasted. They pleaded with Johnny to put the silly idea out of his head or he would end up like the man who put his donkey grazing on the same fort, only to find it dead the very next morning with tiny spears sticking all over its body. But Johnny put their pleadings to one side, saying:
'I know what I'm doing.'
Johnny lived happily in his little wooden hut for a year and a half without anything unusual happening. However, strange things were happening in and around the same fort without Johnny knowing it. The local people when returning home late at night witnessed beautiful lights spinning around this forbidden ground. There were others who heard harp music blend in with Johnny's tin whistle playing, on late evenings as a red sun was gently setting.

KING OF THE FAIRIES

Lo and behold, one night as Johnny remained up very late he heard strange music approaching his little hut.
'Who the devil could this be at this unearthly hour,' Johnny asked himself. Suddenly the little door burst open and in walked the King of the Fairies followed by smaller fairies, all carrying tiny harps. Johnny froze on his stool where he sat reading his bible.
'Fear not earthly man,' said the King of the Fairies. 'You have no need to be alarmed. I've come to advise you regarding your future. If you carry out my instructions you'll become one of the richest men within the Frenchpark area.'
'What is it you want me to do?' asked Johnny nervously.
'I want you to pack some food and milk into your toolbag and hit the Dublin road in early morning. Do not call at any house along the way. After a couple of days walking, you'll come to a crossroads which is close to the town of Mullingar. You will turn left at the crossroads and keep walking until you reach a fairy fort which is much larger than this one. By then it will be nightfall. Inside of this fort is a large cave. You must bed down there for the night. There, you will be told what to do next.'
Johnny Rush hit the road for Dublin the very next morning, as the King of the Fairies had told him. By nightfall he'd only reached Strokestown. He slept in an out-building until morning. A local policeman

saw Johnny leave the building and instructed him to call to an old house where lived a very charitable woman known locally as "The Fairystory Teller". The policeman pointed out the house in question. Johnny thanked him and set out walking in the direction of the house.

Johnny found himself inside a kitchen where a large turf fire sparkled and a tiny skillet pot, hanging above the fire, simmered away for itself. Now, while Johnny was sat by the well scrubbed table eating from a plate of hot porridge mixed with milk and honey, this exceedingly generous old lady asked him if he'd heard of the fairies.

'Of course I have,' said Johnny, as he pushed another spoonful of the produce of the land into his hungry mouth.

The porridge was followed by a big brown mug of strong "tay" and a full round of a sixpenny loaf and believe me, a sixpenny loaf in those days was not anything like the buns that they bake in this day and age. While Johnny was munching away at the round of a loaf, the woman was telling him one of her favourite fairystories. He was about to mention his experience with the same people, when he felt a nudge in his side! and he thought of the warning the King of the Fairies had given him before leaving Frenchpark.

The story the woman was relating to Johnny was about a man who would have acquired a fortune if he had followed the instructions of the Fairy King. Poor Johnny's heart missed a beat, maybe two, when he thought again of what the Fairy King had said: "Do not call at any house along the way."

'Where did this man go wrong?' asked Johnny.

He called to a house along the way where enemies of the fairies lived,' said the woman. 'Had he called to my old mother, God rest her, everything would have been alright,' concluded the woman.

Johnny offered the woman a half crown for her kindness and hospitality but the woman flatly refused.

'It would be an insult to the noble name of Irish hospitality if I was to take money from a travelling man made in the image of Christ himself,' said the woman. 'There was always plenty in this house, because if you give in the name of God, what you give will come back.'

THE CAVE

That night Johnny reached the crossroads outside of Mullingar and, as the Fairy King had told him, he turned left. About an hour later he spotted a large fairy fort on top of a hill and about two hundred yards off the road. He walked up the narrow mossy boreen which led to this fort. He walked slowly around the ring of hawthorn which surrounded this high mount till he came to an opening. Johnny entered the fort and crawled on hands and knees till he reached the cave entrance.

Once inside the cave Johnny searched his pockets will he find the matches and a stump of a candle he'd taken along. He struck a match and applied it to the candle wick as several bats fluttered past him, giving him a nasty fright. A number of stone steps led to a lower chamber of the cave. Slowly Johnny descended the steps and then noticed a huge stone slab at the end of this chamber. He immediately decided it would be his bed.

Johnny used his travelling bag for a pillow and, being jaded after his long walk, he very soon dropped off to sleep. He later awoke to find the chamber beautifully illuminated. In a matter of seconds another Fairy King entered. He was slightly taller than the Frenchpark King and besides, Johnny noticed that he'd also got more golden studs on his crown. He must be the High King thought Johnny, as he stared at the beauty of his unexpected visitor.

'How right you are earthly man,' said the King. 'I can read your thoughts, you know. I am the High King of the Fairies and descended from the High King of Rathcrogan in County Roscommon. Our Frenchpark fort was only established with the coming of the monks to Cloonshanville. Owing to pressures which I cannot mention, we have to close our Frenchpark fort.'

'Now,' said the High King of the Fairies, 'I'm prepared to help you. But you must do everything I tell you and don't ever breathe a word of it until you come to die. Then you will be free to reveal all to your best friend. Your best friend will then have the fairy spell. It will then be up to him or her to keep the secret or lose the spell.'

'What is it you wish me to do, Oh High King?' asked Johnny.

'I want you to return to Frenchpark and in the dead of night when everybody is sleeping, dig a round hole about six paces north of the "hanging tree". When you have reached a depth of forty-eight inches your spade will come against a metal pot filled with gold. Remove the lid carefully and then transfer the gold to your now empty bag, where you keep your tools. Place the lid back on the pot and return the soil to the hole, placing a slender green sod on top.'

'But, Oh High King,' said Johnny 'I have no idea where the "hanging tree" is to be found.'

'That is very true,' said the High King. 'However, all you have to do is to walk home to your fort and a fairy will be waiting to take you to the "hanging tree". A pigeon will coo three times outside your hut, as a warning of the approach of your escorting fairy. Should you fail to keep this secret after you have got the gold, everything you purchase with it will turn to dust.'

THE HANGING TREE

Two days later Johnny returned to Frenchpark. It was very late when he got to his wooden hut within the fort. He bedded down for the night and fell into a deep sleep. He awoke a couple of hours later to the cooing of a pigeon on his doorstep. Johnny leaped out of bed, pulled on his working clothes as fast as he could and took his spade from behind the door. He then opened the door slowly - to find a fairy waiting to escort him to where the "hanging tree" was!!

Of course the Frenchpark natives all knew where this horrible tree was, but Johnny being a stranger, how was he to know? They were amazed when, one night over a pint in Darby's Well, Johnny asked,

'Where about is this tree they call the "hanging tree" ?'

'Where in the name of the Fairies of Pullbawn did you get to know about our hanging tree?' asked the landlord of Darby's Well.

'I was told about it many miles from here,' answered Johnny with a smile.

Johnny knew more than they gave him credit for; what else amazed them was the fact that Johnny Rush was now the best dressed man in the area. He was even better dressed than the old baron himself! He invariably paid for all drinks wherever he went. The biggest puzzle of all though, was the fact that he had stopped work altogether...

A deserted townland

I wrote this poem after visiting a deserted townland whilst holidaying in
my native Roscommon.

The setting sun its shadows cast,
Where laughter once had been,
Once pipers played, an' children strayed,
Old folk their dead did keen.

Where tall trees did grow, an' peasants slaved,
And church bells called to pray,
The simple folk, the nation's cream,
At the end of an Irish day.

The piper's dead, the childred fled,
No dead, or folk to keen,
All, all's gone, their ghosts linger on,
The fields, they still are green.

If the stranger spoiled, an' the peasant toiled,
Though hard his lot had been,
Why? A townland dead, when the stranger's fled
And the flag, it now is green.

True patriots dead, then greed it led
A noble race the strangers' way;
Hate still runs high, men still they die,
At the end of an Irish day.

In music strong, in poem and song
Will the hand of greed decay,
Then a dead "Townland" from its grave will rise,
At the dawn of an Irish day.

To hell or to Connaught
– on foot

MUNSTER IS THE ancestral home of the Dwyer Clan (O'Duibhir). The Frenchpark sprinkling of that Clan has in all probability been there since the mid-seventeenth century.

It was only after I'd read Walter Macken's novel "They Seek the Fair Land" that I commenced to try and place the Frenchpark slice of the Dwyer Clan in some kind of chronological order. It's really a long, sad story commencing with the period when Oliver Cromwell plundered the Irish nation. The rich lands of Munster were confiscated and its noble people forced to flee, either to hell or to the bogs of Connaught. The torture which they incurred along that bloodstained route must have made many of them feel that they were indeed in hell. Some were sold into slavery and there were those who blissfully died along the weary way before reaching their destination.

Those of them who did reach Athlone were meticulously screened before being allowed to cross its historic bridge. Any spark of suspicion by the soldiers either led to a brutal death or deportation. I am fully convinced that somewhere in that bloody line of uncalled misery, there were some families called Dwyer.

Having reached Connaught didn't mean having found freedom. There were still many instances of treachery and brutality. By and large they met with the usual Irish friendliness and hospitality. They were provided with whatever shelter escaped "The Battering Ram". Ragged, bleeding and torn they were treated by their brothers with whatever remained after the plunder. They eventually scattered and built themselves mud huts. It was their firm belief in their god that sustained them.

Shortly after this death march, one of Cromwell's officers called Captain French had commenced to erect a mansion on his confiscated estate at a place called Dungar (Fort of the Gara), later re-named Frenchpark after the captain. After the mansion was erected the captain decided to build a high wall all around the estate. The army of occupation was instructed to "flush out" every known mason in Connaught in order to get the job finished in the quickest time possible. The plundering Irish, as the captain called them, would have to be kept at bay.

The Dwyer stonemasons helped to build that wall for sixpence a day.

Beautiful Sedgeley

In beautiful Sedgeley, 'way up on a hill
There are neatly kept pubs where folk drink their fill
Ancient churches and schools, there's a library close by
Pity the smoke of the "Black Country" pollutes its blue sky
There are sheltered old churchyards where the dead are at rest
Beautiful trees and sweet hawthorn, where the birds snugly nest

There are homely wee tuck shops and super shops down the street
With pleasant smiling faces their customers greet
There's the butchers, the jewellers and the dry cleaners too
There's the old and the young stood in a bus queue
There are neatly clad children on their way to school
And the keen traffic wardens no driver can fool
There's the road worker stood by the old council gate
He lights up a fag as he waits for his mate

Now when midnight it comes and all's gone to rest
The writer then dreams of a place he loves best
In the land of the shamrock, where beauty is seen
He's now a lonely exile in a caravan green

He drops off to sleep, but before very long
He's woke up again, to the chanting of song
'Tis the songbirds of nature, your heart they would thrill
In beautiful Sedgeley, 'way up on a hill

I wrote this poem when working for a travelling firm.
I lived in a caravan at the time.

72

The Concannon brothers

IN KEEPING WITH millions around the world, I was always fascinated with the story and film of the five Sullivan brothers who gave their lives with the American Navy in World War I. It was indeed a very fitting tribute to such a brave and distinguished family. The Americans have been noted for the very respectful manner in which they treat their forces, not to mention the generous remunerations given them.

The recognition that the Sullivan brothers received is indeed in stark contrast to that metered out to the Concannon brothers, who gave their services to the British, also in the first world war. It was in the very early stages of that war, that four Concannon brothers marched bravely into a Cheshire recruiting office and together offered their services to the war effort.

It was only when the third Concannon brother "plumped" his name in a typical musical west of Ireland accent, that the old recruiting officer woke up to the fact that something unusual was taking shape. The officer paused and stared questioningly at his latest raw recruit.

'Concannon!' shouted the uniformed gentleman in a rather extra-loud tone of voice. 'I have just enlisted two by that same surname. Are you related to the others?' he asked.

'We are of course related,' replied Concannon number three. 'In fact we are lawful brothers,' he added.

'Very good old chap! Very good indeed! We're hoping to get more of your type,' he added with a grin. 'However, I must warn you that as soon as you sign on the dotted line, you will be in the British army. From then on you will be required to address your superior officers as SIR, understood?'

'You have made yourself perfectly clearly, SIR. I will try to remember that, SIR,' replied the Irishman, in an extra-loud tone of voice. The Concannons were strong, brave, intelligent men, who believed that "SIRs" never won a war.

'OK Concannon! On your way. We will be in touch with you later,' ended the officer, shouting in a clearly authoritarian tone, 'next!'

It was then that Concannon number four marched firmly towards the officer's desk and stood at attention. The old war dog stared at his new arrival questioningly, as if he had already detected a resemblance to the three gone before.

'What is your name?' queried the officer.

'Doctor Thomas Concannon,' came the curt reply.

'*Doctor* Thomas Concannon!' repeated the officer, looking rather startled. 'I have here on my desk the names of three recruits by that same familiar surname, who say they are brothers. Are you another of the same brood?' asked the now puzzled Englishman.

'I am one of the same family, sir. In fact I am a brother of the other three, sir.'

'Most extraordinary, old chap! Most extraordinary!' said the amused officer. 'Tell me,' he continued, 'do you Concannon brothers figure that you are going to win this war all on your own?'

'Not really. But we'll have a bloody good try, sir,' replied the doctor.

'I shall have this unique experience of mine brought to the notice of my superiors, Concannon!' said the officer. 'There is one thing, however, that puzzles me,' he continued, 'it is the title of "doctor". Are you really a doctor?' he asked.

'Of course I am a doctor,' replied the new recruit.

'But you have also stated that you are a farm worker' said the officer. 'I think Concannon, that you have some explaining to do,' demanded the officer.

'I can explain, sir,' replied the doctor.

'Very well then, go ahead,' said the now impatient officer.

'It is fair to say that I am not a doctor in the medical sense that I studied medicine. But I was born the seventh son of a seventh son. This has bestowed upon me the power to cure ringworm and other skin diseases, by simply placing my right hand upon the effected skin area.'

'I find that story very difficult to believe, Concannon!' said the officer. 'Will you please explain how you came to acquire this, whatever it is?'

'I will indeed, sir,' replied the doctor. 'On the night that I was born, the local midwife instructed my father to go out and find a large worm. It being the month of November, to find a worm small or big was indeed a formidable task.

It was hours later, I am told, that my father returned with a large worm concealed in a silver snuffbox. The midwife then removed the worm from its hiding place and placed it in the palm of my right hand. She then closed my hand and held it tightly between her two hands. In a matter of minutes, the harmless creature was dead.'

'The dead worm was then placed in a tiny silver pan and roasted above a sparkling turf fire. It was then ground into powder and mixed in warm milk, which was taken from a young, white cow. The mixture was then put into a tiny silver cup which was found buried deep down in a bog many years before. The cup was then given to the midwife who fed it to me with a tiny wooden spoon that was found in a nearby fairy fort, by my great grandmother on a May morn.'

'Over the years I have cured countless people who suffered from skin trouble. Shall I continue, sir?' asked the doctor.

'Carry on. It sounds very interesting, but daft,' said the puzzled officer.

'OK, sir. Whenever I went fishing, which was often, I always had to ask somebody to place the worm or grub on my hook. If I chanced to touch it, death would be instantaneous.'

'Can you get people to testify to all or most of what you've just told me?' asked the seemingly interested officer.

'I can take more than a dozen Englishmen and women in this very area to testify that I did cure their ringworm after their own doctor had failed,' replied the doctor.

'An incredible story if ever I heard one,' said the officer. 'However, in view of what I have heard, that is the fact that you Concannon brothers seem to have come from an heroic and distinguished family, I will place the title "Doctor" after, but not before your name. I find it rather amusing the way you Irish acquire titles,' stated the "titled gentleman". 'Next!' boomed the officer.

The Concannon brothers were born in the townland of Sheepwalk, about two miles from the town of Frenchpark in the County Roscommon. There were, as already stated, seven brothers and two sisters. The Concannon family is now extinct. One sister did marry locally and raised a fine family of men and women, all of which are still with us. Another matter of some interest is the fact that the midwife, mentioned earlier in my story, was my great grandmother whose marriage name was Maxwell, but was affectionately known as Betty Sampey. Actually she was referred to in those days as a "handy woman".

It was in the summer of 1938 as a young lad, that I came face to face with "Doctor" Thomas Concannon. Our meeting took place in a country public house, not very far from the town of Northwich. It was called The Tunnel Tap. I was introduced to him by an old neighbour from back home. He was extremely delighted to have met me, having known all of my people. I had heard of him dozens of times. In fact the name and fame of the Concannon family was a household word in the part of County Roscommon where we both came from.

I t would be almost impossible for me to recall the entire conversation that passed between myself and the doctor on that memorable day. But I did retain enough to help me to put this story together. The doctor had never lost touch of the gift he received from my great grandmother, Betty Sampey on the night he was born. He was still an active man both physically and in the administration of his now undisputed cures.

The story of his magic had spread throughout Cheshire and beyond. It was so often related in the local public houses, of the days when the doctor's English mates would find a live worm and place it on the floor in front of the "Doc" as they affectionately called him. The "Doc" would then make a ring with the forefinger of his right hand around the harmless creature. It would wriggle for a few minutes within the ring and then die. The proof was, indeed if proof was needed, for an unbeliever to find another worm, then make an imaginary ring around it and wait. In a matter of seconds the lucky creature would crawl away to safety.

I parted with my doctor friend that day, never to see him again. He died in the midst of the second world war. He was buried with full military honours. His many English friends had seen to that. All of his soldier brothers had preceded him in death. All survived World War I. In fact, at least one, if not two of them were awarded medals on the battlefield, for bravery in the face of the enemy.

So ends my story, a story that has been lying dormant for far too long.

An extraordinary
Mayo man

WHEN I WAS scarcely more than a toddler - and that's a few moons ago
- a fairly regular visitor to our district in North Roscommon was a man
called Peter Towey. I still have a fairly vivid recollection of what he looked
like. He was tall, six foot or over and of slim build. His dark hair was
combed straight back.

Whenever I saw him walking along a country lane or boreen, I always
got the impression that he walked on air. His feet never seemed to touch the
ground! What's more, tucked underneath Peter's arm was an old brown case.
Every child soon got to know the secret of this magic case. Peter was a noted
fiddle player.

He usually came about mid September and remained for the greater part of the winter months. He usually rented an old unoccupied farm cottage, where he gave lessons on the fiddle to any boy or girl anxious to learn and produced some rare talent, including the late Tom "Sweeper" Mulvehill of Frenchpark who later became famous throughout the U.S.A.

Music was but one of this unique man's talents. He was also, for a number of years, Ireland's leading traditional dancer. He produced at least one all Ireland winner, Tim Cassidy also of Frenchpark.

He also had another unique talent which one never sees nowadays. He could play and dance a hornpipe simultaneously. "The Boys of Bluehill" was his favourite - better known in North Roscommon as "Towey's Hornpipe".

One fine day in early February, Peter said farewell to the people of the district and set out in the direction of his native Mayo, on foot as usual. Many years passed, but nothing was heard of Peter. The older people would often ask,

'I wonder whatever became of poor Peter Towey?'

It was during the last war, I was cutting a hedge close to the Boyle-Frenchpark road. I saw coming towards me a tall, slim, grey-haired and wrinkled old man. He was carrying an old brown case. Yes, it was "old" Peter Towey.

We talked for a while about the good ould days. It was quite obvious that this great "musical rolling stone" hadn't gathered the kind of "moss" people are reaching out for today. But his was a leading part in passing on a very great tradition.

A car came round the corner, Peter thumbed it down and climbed aboard. We shook hands for the last time before the car sped off in the direction of Boyle town. Peter Towey disappeared from my view in a cloud of dust.

He must have long since passed onto his eternal reward. May his soul rest in peace.

Waiting at the crossroads
- for Tom Waters

It was a hardy, frosty Christmas Eve morning, around the mid-fifties. I was waiting at the Frenchpark crossroads for Tom Waters to arrive with a glut of expected Christmas mail. The countryside which adorns this welcoming town in those days was alive with countless crows, noisily manoeuvring as if undecided whether to take to the open country or remain in their warm nests.

Andy McManus, who was our senior postman at the time, appeared in the grey dawn, his protective clothing tucked neatly under his right arm. This was a sure sign that rain was on the way, for amongst other important matters, Andy was a judge of the weather. We both talked in low tones for a few minutes before deciding to move to Michael Healy's place for a couple of "half-ones", knowing very well that Tom Waters would be late because of the Christmas rush. This in fact was an annual ritual.

The hall door of Healy's place was opened to us by Mrs Healy affectionately known as "Ciss". She certainly had a heart of gold. After we'd exchanged seasonal greetings Ciss directed us towards the kitchen while she entered the bar, appearing minutes later with two large whiskeys - on the house of course. This friendly gesture was followed by mugs of strong "tay". It must have been at least six half-ones later when the familiar sound of the Thames 800 brought myself and Andy to our feet. Tom Waters had arrived.

Reluctantly we both left the roasting turf fire and the warmer hospitality of Ciss Healy behind and headed off in the direction of the post office. There we joined our other colleagues and the Gannon sisters who owned the post office at the time, in the laborious task of removing the cumbersome mailbags from the van and slinging them through the open doorway. Tom's longish shabby jacket was the colour of the bags.

Tom hit the road to Ballinagare while myself, Andy, the late James McManus and Walter Healy, a son of our pleasant hostess, set about the task of sorting this huge volume of greetings. Thanks to the late Gannon sisters, everything moved methodically.

Now, after a very pleasant Christmas in Ireland with members of my family, I returned to Leeds in mid-January 1992. In the course of unpacking, a book that my son Vincent had presented me with before leaving, dropped on the floor, its intriguing title "Jiving at the Crossroads" caught my attention. 'What real interest could a man of my years have in jiving,' I murmured. I decided that the only way to find out was to read it.

I hadn't got far till I discovered that the author of this interesting book was John Waters, a son of Tom Waters, who was once my colleague and friend. I'm not surprised that John Waters has delved into politics. His late father would spare a few minutes any day to discuss some passing political issue. Tom did have strong views he never feared to express.

Inexperience does not allow me to give as full and frank a review of this work as it deserves. It's the kind of book that once you commence to read it, you're loth to put it to one side while you're having your dinner. It gives a very accurate and revealing account of the pleasantries and of course the intrigue which is part and parcel of politics everywhere. It's a mixture of enlightenment and pleasure. It should appeal to people of voting age, particularly the youth.

My first impression of this book's title "Jiving at the Crossroads" was that it did not seem to fit in with its revealing contents. However, it later occurred to me that for centuries Irish politics has been at a crossroads with one sign pointing in one particular direction. I very much doubt if over the past seventy years, Ireland's politicians have ever tried to find where the three missing signs could lead them. Never mind. We know that the politicians will jive, strive and even kiss babies, if it gets them votes. Some have even tried singing.

The lilter

Their gifted vocal cords had found a special honoured place,
Amongst the learned Brehon, the Fili and the Bard,
In ancient time. Beyond an unrecorded misty space,
Long before the magical harp an' lute in Tara's Hall was heard.
This musical songbird gift, has lingered on and on,
Through needless famine. Through strife. Through mirth and tears.
Reminding us of our heroic dead, long past and gone,
Lilting has not lost its magic with the passing of the years.
No, lilting has not lost its magic with the passing of the years.
Irish folk have gathered ere' the harvest had been won,
To sing the praises of their giver and to lilt away their fears.
'Round some glowing turf fire, their vocal cords served dancers,
everyone.
And as a winter dawn is breaking, over mountain and over bog,
The lilter from the céilí homeward journeyed, his mind engrossed
in music new.
Pauses a moment, lost notes to recall. He's rudely interrupted by the
barking of a dog.
At last he's reached the fairy fort, his troubles now, are few.

A strange vision

This story received a Commendation from The Irish Post

As I BECOME more deeply absorbed in peaceful retirement, I invariably attend daily mass in St Anne's Cathedral in Leeds. For the past couple of years I've been fascinated by the presence of an old decrepit man crouched in a dark corner near the side door, his frost bitten lips moving in prayer. He slips out silently towards the end of mass and takes up a position on the stone steps. His right hand extended for help, he thanks his donors in a husky tone of voice.

One day I approached this "but for the grace of God, there goes I", in an effort to try and offer a consoling word, also to try and ferret out how he had dropped below the bottom rung. He was very reluctant to engage in conversation and when in the end he decided to utter a few incoherent words, I discovered two things. One, he had a speech impediment; the other, he spoke with an Irish accent.

On my way home, as the number 4 bus jerked its cumbersome way through the dense traffic, "the least of things sat on the Cathedral steps" kept nagging at my conscience. After all, I'm a tiny fraction of that so-called caring society that's supposed to extend a helping hand towards its less fortunate fellow humans. This poor wretch had, I thought, perhaps forgotten who he was. I decided there and then to create his past.

The bus came to a halt. As I stepped onto the pavement, a hazy vision entered that yet to be fully explored "continent" the brain. I saw the figure of a middle-aged woman holding a baby in her arms. On her right was a stocky man in his mid-forties and on her left an old priest. On the priest's left stood a boy and girl in their late teens. The name Simon was repeated a number of times by the priest. I had found my man's name for a start, or so I thought. However, I was later to be sadly disappointed.

My intuition told me that Simon was the fourth child of four boys but who their parents were I could not figure out. They eked out a living on a small farm, somewhere in rural Ireland. They were a strictly honest family, devoutly religious and fond of fishing. It was one of many countless homes in the Ireland of the day where the "Song of the Rosary" could be heard echoing across the dew-drenched meadows on a late evening, accompanied by the tunefulness of the cooing pigeons and friendly corncrakes.

Simon is now a growing lad. He's getting on fairly well in the two-roomed school near his home. However, I have a feeling that his parents thought Simon's educational standards fell short of that of his older brothers. The oldest boy joined the priesthood and died prematurely in Korea. The next in line emigrated to America; while the third inherited the little farm. Simon worked for a period with the local County Council.

L ater, Simon decided to join his brother in America but failed his test at the American Consul in Dublin. He had now no choice but to hit the road for England. One morning he packed his case, bid farewell to his brother and with a weary heart walked slowly up the narrow boreen which led to the main bus route. He'd set out on the first leg of a weary journey.

It was misting rain as Simon made his way out of a Leeds Railway Station. It was in the early spring of 1938. He would be rather amazed at the countless people scurrying in all directions. Back home, the only time people seemed to rush was if they felt they were late for mass. He made his way into a nearby café to devour a hearty breakfast.

In the days before World War II, work was very hard to come by. However, given the influence of an Irish priest, Simon found a job and settled in an Irish lodging house. He soon became acquainted with his fellow Irishmen who'd arrived there long before him. They led him invariably to the choice of beer-houses, some of which left much to be desired in those days.

Before leaving his native Ireland, Simon had been a strict teetotaller.

One night at a dance he met and fell in love with a Scotch lass called Betty. As the weeks passed he learned to dodge the beer-shops for the girl he loved. Betty worked in a local shoe factory. They had arranged to be married in the Autumn of 1939, but the war clouds which had gathered over Europe at that moment in time had darkened their desires.

Simon returned to his native Ireland for Christmas. War had broken out. He remained over the festive season and enjoyed the many jovial events which characterised the period of goodwill in those days. His brother had married a local girl. She did her utmost to prevent Simon returning to England fearing his involvement in the war.

'After all, it was a war that could be easily avoided,' she declared.

Simon returned to Leeds in February 1940, to discover that many of his pals had been drafted into the war effort. His Scottish lover Betty had left the shoe factory and taken a more remunerative job in a munitions works. Simon found a job in the same factory and in the course of a few months they were married.

Shortly after their marriage the army authorities commenced chasing Simon. His many pleadings of Irish nationality were regarded as a big joke. Many years later it suddenly transpired just how right they were. Such terms as "hostages" or "human shields" were unheard of or expediently brushed aside in those days. Simon was whisked across the channel to fight for "King and country".

Simon's wife Betty remained in her job. There were many letters of love and hope exchanged between them in the years that elapsed. Then one morning in late 1943, Betty's factory received a direct hit in the course of which, amongst many others, Betty was killed.

In the meantime over in a French hospital her husband was undergoing treatment following wounds received in the course of a bomb explosion. He was due home on leave but his wounds put paid to that. Simon and his first and last love were in a split second on that fatal morning parted for ever, at least in this life.

Simon returned to Leeds in 1944 a broken, shell-shocked man. He was unable to take up employment for a considerable length of time. His army back-pay soon ran out. His application for army pension was also regarded as a joke since he had not been in army service long enough to qualify. Besides, he was treated as a conscript.

He did find the odd job which to him, with his inbred dignity, he found to be very degrading. As Simon gradually slid down the social ladder, he got into bad company and eventually fell foul of the law. He served a prison term which was for him the last straw. After his release his only consolation was to visit the grave of his Betty, as he called her. Nowadays he drinks cheap wine whenever he can afford it and sometimes finds a bed in a police cell where he is treated as a harmless layabout.

One morning on my way out of church, I cautiously approached Simon in an effort to try and find out if my creation of his past had any link or connection at all with the man. After some persuasion and a little bribery, I found that his real name was John and not Simon. Disappointed I commenced to move away. He raised a weathered hand, then stared at me with sad moistened eyes and in a broken voice uttered the following words:

'If my Betty...had lived...I'd not have...ended up...this way.'

The miracle of
Mount Saint Mary's

AFTER THE ABORTIVE rebellion of 1798 and up until almost the middle of the nineteenth century, the Irish people enjoyed a kind of uneasy peace and frugal comfort. Prior to that they did have their "lion's share" of undeserved troubles. Ireland's population had at that period reached an all time figure of eight million plus. There was precious little emigration, just a trickle of invariably men, who believed that the fields were that much greener beyond the shores of their native Ireland.

A percentage of this trickle found its way to Yorkshire, where some stayed in Leeds at a slummish area called Richmond Hill, euphemistically known at a later stage as "The Bank". The first contingent of Irish arriving there were very soon recruited for the not very enviable task of cutting their end of the Leeds to Liverpool Canal. Their contact with the homeland meant that more were soon to join them.

It was not until 1824 that a steep escalation of Irish began to be very noticeable on The Bank. The reason for this sudden influx was the introduction of the Tariff Export Act, imposed on Ireland by the British Government for the protection of their own industries. This Act had a devastating effect on Irish industry, particularly its weaving. The handlooms began to grind to a halt.

From 1824 onwards the population of Irish both in Yorkshire and Lancashire had grown rapidly. Many of the Irish were skilled particularly in the weaving trade, as well as in stone work. The plot behind the Tariff Act now begins to unfold. Yorkshire being one of the homes of the weaving trade, Irish skill was there for the taking.

In addition to the weaving, another type of employment which the Irish were placed in, was the building of the first railway line. Tens of thousands of tons of solid rock had to be excavated from the centre of The Bank by crowbar, pick and shovel. The hours were many, the wages meagre and the conditions atrocious. However, much worse was to follow.

The population of Irish now living, or rather existing, on The Bank had increased to the two thousand mark, made up of men, women and children. A vast deterioration in living conditions soon became apparent. There was precious little sympathy and far less official attention paid to their social needs. They were described by the media as "unskilled, uncouth and uneducated".

The Roman Catholic Church was at a very low ebb in the England of the period in question. It wasn't until 1845 that the first anglican church was built on The Bank, which gives us some idea of how the spiritual needs of the Irish catholic population were being catered for. It looked as if the Good Lord had abandoned His people. But He had not.

On the very day that the anglican church was opened, an anglican minister, Dr Newman, was received into the Catholic Church; two more anglican ministers Dr Keble and Dr Pucey, followed later. All of them were intellectuals and described as "The Brainchild of the Experimental Church of Catholicity".

By the year 1851, owing to the famine of 1846-47 - officially recorded in England as "a strange Irish disease" - the population of Irish now struggling for an existence on The Bank, had risen to well beyond the six thousand mark. The insanitary conditions of those people cannot be described in words alone. Ash middens had to be used as toilets. This extremely unhygenic situation led to diseases of various kinds. The cholera and typhus which swept Europe at the time, found its way to Britain and The Bank. Hundreds of men, women and children found premature graves, without the consoling prayers of a catholic priest.

In the midst of all this degradation the Irish had not lost their deep faith handed down to them over the centuries. On any night before retiring to their humble beds, the "Song of the Rosary" could be heard echoing, in Gaelic and often in tears, along the muddy waters of the River Aire.

It was on the 2nd of April 1851 that seven more anglican ministers were received into the Catholic Church. They were as follows: Rev G Crawley, Rev T Minster, Rev M Ward, Rev J Neville, Rev S Roach, Rev H Comes and Rev M Lewthwaite. This ceremony took place in St Anne's Church, The Headrow, Leeds. All of them together with the earlier conversions set for themselves the monumental task, as now ordinary laymen, of caring for the spiritual needs of the entire catholic population of Leeds.

They took up residence at a "Cottage Orphanage" on The Bank where they devoted much of their spare time catering for the needs of those children who had lost their parents in such tragic circumstances. It must also be remembered that they had to try and overcome the backlash that their conversion to the Roman Catholic Church had aroused. The story of their heroic efforts deserves to be passed on.

It was on the morning of 24th May 1853 that the foundation of the first catholic church on The Bank was blessed by Bishop Briggs. This service took place under a marquee, in the exact spot where in the year 1643 on 23rd January, General Fairfax had his tent erected after he'd captured Leeds from the Marquis of Newcastle. Father Pinet, the French priest in charge of building the church, wrote in his diary: "Cannon smoke is just being replaced by sweet smelling incense".

Slowly and laboriously the church began to appear on Richmond Hill, amidst prayer, slavery, death, sweat and tears. But on the 2nd May 1854, a terrible thunderstorm hit the north of England and also the growing church on The Bank, damaging much of the hard won work and killing three Irishmen: John Cummins, John Reilly and John McDorrach. Many more were seriously injured. This seemed "the last straw" but more was to follow.

Money - "the root of all evil" - began to run out. This was due mainly to the discovery of a mineshaft beneath the foundation, which accounted for much extra cost both in materials and labour. At the same time the value of land in the north of England began to soar, on account of the growing industry and call for extra housing.

A greedy mortgager to whom the Oblate Mission owed £1,000 demanded payment of that sum, not later than the last day of November 1854. If the Mission failed to pay within the given time, work would have to cease forthwith and furthermore, the work already undertaken would have to be demolished. But the indomitable Father Pinet and his Irish people stood firm.

The good priest called his people together and as a result a novena was started to a French Saint named Joseph Benedict Labre, known in France as "The Beggarman Saint". The novena carried on for nine days and on the ninth day, as Father Pinet and his congregation were ending this service, a well-dressed man walked smartly past the praying people and just as the priest was making the sign of the cross, he tapped him on the shoulder, handed him a small black bag, turned sharply around and made a quick exit.

The black bag was found to contain £1,000 in gold. The donor was never located. A specially carved altar was later erected within the church, dedicated to Saint Joseph Benedict Labre "The Beggarman Saint".

It was on the 14th February 1853 that three heroic nuns arrived in Leeds from their Oblate Order in France, in a violent snowstorm. They were Sister Joseph a Mrs Caroline Doratt nee Robertson, belonging to a very rich family of Jamaican Planters and Sister Ignatius, Lady Harris of Scotland; both widowed before joining the Oblate Order. The third nun was Sister Geddes who belonged to a distinguished Yorkshire family.

Their coach got stuck in the snow at the foot of The Bank forcing them to abandon the coach and crawl hand and foot up the steep hill to the Cottage Orphanage. Lighted candles in every window greeted their arrival. Their Herculean task was to open an Oblate House on The Bank, a task which they fulfilled with the utmost courage and determination. Their educational achievements have been stunning and rewarding.

Mount Saint Mary's was officially opened on the 29th July 1857. A large attendance of 20,000 lined the route leading to the church, to receive the blessings of His Eminence Cardinal Wiseman, Monsignor de Mazenod, Bishop of Marseilles, Dr John Manning and Bishop John Briggs, as their coaches moved slowly past jubilant crowds and brilliantly decorated streets.

This was indeed in deep contrast to what William Osborn had to say about The Bank, when in 1857 he penned the following lines:

"The Aire below is doubly dyed and dammed,
The air above, with lurid smoke is crammed."

Today, one hundred and thirty-odd years later, Mount Saint Mary's is again fighting for its survival as dwindling congregations threaten its future. But once again, the cream of the "old stock" have come to its rescue. It is after all, the second largest church in England.

I am indebted to Mr Patrick Gavin, 15 East Park Street, Leeds, lecturer and historian, also a member of Mount Saint Mary's History Society, for his valuable assistance in the researching of this article.

Philosophy?

I AM TOLD that "Agorazein" is a word in the Greek language having no equivalent in any other language. Its meaning, according to the Greeks of ancient times, was to jog or saunter around kind of aimlessly and in pensive mood. It also meant engaging in conversation with others along their path. There were many thousands of such people in Greece. They did not engage in any kind of laborious work, nor did they have to, because while there might have been as many as twenty thousand such men studying the stars, there were also countless slaves - mainly foreign - who did their work for them.

There were schools where such people studied but their main custom was to engage in debate. They were also referred to as "sages" in those far off days. Their philosophies have been passed on for posterity from as far back as 600 BC. While we do give the Greeks much credit for being the first philosophers, it still remains to be told if there were indeed philosophers of a kind in other parts of the world, at the time that the Greeks were doing their thinking.

For example, in the period many moons before the coming of Christ there were sages, or what was described as Bards, in ancient Ireland and Celtic Britain. Away back before the coming of Saint Patrick the Bards of Ireland used to meet at a place called Tara in the County Meath, which was at that time the capital of Ireland and also where the High King of Ireland resided.

Like the Greek philosophers they too were not very concerned about work and also like the Greek thinkers, they also had slaves to do their work. Indeed those were the days when the Irish often raided Britain and brought back many slaves to Ireland. This was, of course, the manner with which Patrick first arrived in Ireland in the very early fifth century. Patrick later made his miraculous escape, eventually arriving in Gaul now known as France.

After he'd been educated in Gaul and ordained to the priesthood, Patrick heard the voices of the pagan Irish calling. He returned to Ireland in the year 432 AD and set about teaching the Irish people the message of Christ. The learned Bards took a deep liking to this "strange" man and chiefly because of that, Christianity spread quickly throughout Ireland. This was to be a "Godsend" to Europe later, when Irish scholars and priests brought learning, culture and the Word of God to a shattered Europe. History has recorded that the Bards of the fifth century Ireland looked upon Saint Patrick as a very poorly educated man. The big question is: was Greek philosophy being studied in Ireland before Saint Patrick's time, or did the Irish have their own brand of philosophy?

Much has been written by modern philosophers and psychologists about the mind and its relationship to the human body, ever since the days of Socrates and Saint Patrick. The question which seems to have remained unanswered since those far off days: is the mind a physical part of the body or a separate invisible something that finds its way through an unknown region after death?

I'm certainly no philosopher, nor have I ever delved into the depths of this "mind-boggling" subject. Although in my younger days over in Ireland, we did have a philosopher of a very interesting kind in almost every townland. Mind you, I very much regret to have to say that they did not always get the credit they so dearly deserved. Let me hasten to add, that I am by no means mixing my Irish philosophers with my Irish story-tellers. They were leagues apart.

There is, however, one in particular which leaps to my humble mind. I called to see him in the course of a visit to my native Roscommon some years back. He was ninety-seven at the time. In all the years that I'd known him, I'd always regarded him as the nearest to "that gift" as one could find. I had not met up with the man in years before that, yet the first question he asked me was,

'How's your twelve grandchildren goin' on?' I was amazed and stunned by the fact that he knew that I had twelve grandchildren.

In the course of our discussion he went on to talk about the state of the world and its growing crime and violence. He thought it had quadrupled in the course of his long life. He also blamed (to use his term) "the growing greed of a privileged minority" for this tragic state of affairs. The unequal distribution of the world's resources he described as becoming more "unequal" with the passage of time.

'The only sin', he continued, 'that I can't accuse them of is *sloth*, all the others they are guilty of.'

The question of the soul and its relationship to the physical body brought a sparkle to his ageing blue eyes. The mind, he was fully convinced, is by no means a physical part of the body, in so far that when death claims the body, the soul or mind soars into an unknown region. There is a region for the good soul and another for the bad soul. To elaborate on that statement, he contended, would be to judge and he was not competent to judge.

The brilliance with which unbelievers could write amazed him because he himself did not have much of an education. All his knowledge he claimed, came from a power or intellect out there in the great unknown. He was fully convinced that his mind was directly in touch with a power outside of the planet earth. Where the agnostics or unbelievers got their inspiration from always puzzled him.

'This proves', he continued, 'That there must certainly be a power out there who is the inspirator of evil. The growing evil in our tiny part of the great universe is ample evidence of this theory', he added.

(His old grandmother once told him of a man who sold his soul to the devil. In her day all one had to do was to find a briar with both its ends in the ground. By crawling beneath the briar three times in the name of the devil, any request would be granted. This particular man wished for riches and got them in abundance. However, the night he died a huge gap appeared in the gable of his house through which his soul passed on its way to a satanic environment.)

And when questioned about abortion and birth control, he paused for a minute and then replied:

'My mother was the youngest of nine of a family. If my grandmother had had her aborted I would not be talking to you today. Furthermore', he continued, 'All this upset in human nature is the brain-child of the greedy ruling minority. They have betrayed the masses and spat in the face of God.'

Before leaving I shook his worn and aged hand and thanked him for the chat.

'You're very welcome', said he. Then his blue eyes began to moisten. 'I won't be seein' you anymore', he said in a broken voice. He died shortly after. Hopefully, his soul passed on to that region he so often dreamed of in the course of his ninety-seven years. He was a simple peasant farmer called Edmond Murren.

A musical ass-ociation

It WAS ONE of those late harvest evenings, when most of the corn had been carried in from the many surrounding fields that dotted the small farming neighbourhood. Hundreds of crows blackened the stubble, happily cawing as they made a hearty meal of whatever corn was lost in the process.

A huge red ball of a sun hung lazily above the distant blue mountain, drawing a last breath before disappearing suddenly to illuminate the underworld. A few remaining swallows flew high as they fed on the wing, which was a true sign that the next day would be fine. A mini-harvest festival was just about to start at our house.

Those were the days of my carefree youth which, although many moons ago, I can vividly remember with pride. Myself and my late dad (RIP) was after putting the last of the produce from the road-field into our

93

barn, making sure that the door hasp was tightly fitted in the catch, so that our cute donkey Black Bess, would not succeed in making an entry.

It really annoys me whenever I hear the saying "As thick as a donkey". In the townland where I first saw the light there was another saying "As cute as Dwyer's donkey". Whenever a neighbour borrowed Black Bess to go to the local market, she would limp pathetically all the way there and canter all the way home! In the end no-one dared to borrow her.

The last man to do so was a very cantankerous fellow. He had some lambs to take to the local butcher. They'd almost become fully grown sheep by the time he got there. To add to his troubles, he was booked by a civic Guard for working a lame ass. On his way home he was again booked by another Guard for dangerous driving. Later when the Guards compared notes, the matter was dropped. This incident later became a fireside tale of winter nights.

Now let us get back to the harvest festival. The main reason why it was held at our place was the fact that my late mother (RIP) was a very lively melodeon player. Besides, she was also a great cook and her treacle cakes with plenty of raisins in, was another attraction.

As the light faded, the good old neighbours tripped across dew-moistened pastures, down shady, mossy boreens and over spikey stubble in order to be at our harvest festival. There were fiddles, flutes and one concertina. There was also the ould bodhrán which hung above the rod-cradle the night I was born. There was also the famous lilter, Mick Quinn.

After supper each got hold of their respective seats and marched out to Eugene's Boreen in front of our house to partake in a prolonged session of traditional music and dance. There was a large stone flagged patch nearby. It can be truthfully stated that every known Irish dance took place on that same patch. The boreen was named after a man called Eugene, who in more distant times had a right to the pass.

As the music and dance got under way, our Black Bess now grazing peacefully in a distant pasture field, began to move slowly in the direction of the now jubilant gathering. She would move about a dozen paces, then turn her head to one side in the manner of an adjudicator who'd detected an error in the rhythm of the music, that filled the air for miles around.

When Black Bess reached the fence that divided the field from the boreen, she came to a sudden halt. Raising her head high into the air she commenced to bray in a manner I'd not heard before, completely drowning the music. Everybody was charmed by this standing ovation, coming as it did from a breed of animal that was saddled with everybody's thickheadedness down the centuries.

All the neighbouring donkeys joined in and there wasn't an ass for miles distant who didn't pay its respects to Dwyer's harvest festival. The cultural gathering really enjoyed its donkey audience and when the laughter that this unusual incident caused had died away, entertainment was resumed with the Roscommon Set.

Black Bess waited until the dance had got well under way before walking slowly in the direction of our barn. She paused for some time in front of its red door, then grabbed the hasp in her strong teeth and snatched it clean out of its catch. She then pushed the door open with her head and stepped gingerly inside. Only the lilter Mick Quinn noticed Black Bess' crafty move. He left the old girl in peace till the hilarious night had ended.

Happy to meet, sorry to part

Happy to meet, sorry to part...

Where glows the Irish hearth with peat
Where lives a subtle spell
The faint blue smoke, the gentle heat
The moorland odours tell

Happy to meet, sorry to part...

White sandy roads winding to the edge
Of bare, untamed land
Where dry stone wall or ragged hedge
Runs wide on either hand

Happy to meet, sorry to part...

The tales of magic love, or alms
From days when princes met
To listen to the lay that charms
The Connaught peasant yet

Happy to meet, sorry to part...

Where honour shines through passions dire
Where beauty blends with mirth
Where wild hearts never did aspire
Wholly for the things of earth
And when the weavering wreaths ascend
Blue in the evening air
The soul of Ireland seems to bend
Above her children there

My céilí lass

By the haunting ruins of a céilí cot, in a homely sheltered glade,
In autumn haze one evenin' late, in pensive mood I strayed.
A familiar voice in the harvest air! It came from out the sky,
"In that céilí cot we'll dance no more,
My dancing lad and I"

As our schooling days had blithely passed, to the céilí cot we'd stray,
To join the senior céilí folk and to hear the fiddlers play.
Shyly, eagerly, hand in hand, to emulate their steps we'd try.
In carefree days of yore, we danced galore,
My céilí lass and I

In autumn haze one early morn' she quietly passed away,
As her kith and kin assembled at her bedside, for to pray.
Far, far away in a sheltered glade, was heard the banshee cry,
In that céilí cot we'll dance no more,
My céilí lass and I

*In loving memory of my late wife Kathleen. Traditional singer
and céilí dancer who died prematurely in Leeds on 3rd August 1969 R.I.P.*